CLIVE BARKER was bo[rn...]
He is the author of *The Book[...]*
The Damnation Game, *Weaveworld*, *Cabal*, *The Great and Secret Show*, *The Hellbound Heart*, *Imajica* and *The Thief of Always*. In addition to his work as a novelist and short story writer, he is also an accomplished illustrator and writes, directs and produces for the stage and screen. His spectacular films the *Hellraiser* trilogy, *Nightbreed* and *Candyman* bring his unique and indelible vision of modern horror to celluloid and video life. Barker uses all aspects of popular culture to substantiate his extraordinary insight into the menacing present. Millions of readers and filmgoers have been captivated by Barker's prodigious talents; now graphic novel adaptations of his stories add a further dimension to his hold on the popular imagination. Clive Barker lives in Los Angeles, where he continues his love affair with the bizarre, the perverse and the terrifying.

INTERNATIONAL ACCLAIM FOR
CLIVE BARKER:

'Barker is so good I am almost tongue-tied. What Barker does makes the rest of us look like we've been asleep for the last ten years.'

STEPHEN KING

'A powerful and fascinating writer with a brilliant imagination.'

J.G.BALLARD

'Clive Barker has been an amazing writer from his first appearance, with great gifts of invention and commitment to his own vision stamped on every page.'

PETER STRAUB

THE ARTISTS

Stewart Stanyard

is an illustrator, painter and comic book artist who also
enjoys playing the violin and strumming a guitar in a room
full of other people strumming guitars. He was born in
1962 in Beaver Falls, Pennsylvania, and studied illustration
at the Academy of Art College in San Francisco. He has
worked for such magazines as *A+*, *Mix*, *Watch*, and
The Golden Road. His recent work includes Eclipse's
Savings and Loan Scandal trading cards, and an *Anxiety
Times* short story. He shares his life with his wife Denise
and their cat Sushi, and is an avid fan of the Twilight Zone.

Stewart writes: I would like to offer special thanks to
Denise Stanyard and Fred Sommer for modelling,
Paula Sommer for the London reference, and my father
Paul Stanyard for his genes.

The artwork in this book is dedicated to the loving memory
of my sister Christina Lynn Stanyard.

Hector Gomez

was born in Argentina and now lives in Brazil. He has had
two graphic novels published in Brazil, *Samsara* and
Amazing Muchachas. He works as an illustrator for
mainstream magazines and exhibits canvases at exhibitions.
His work for Eclipse includes artwork for Clive Barker's
How Spoilers Bleed. His covers for Malibu Comics include
Dollman, Rocket Ranger, Jungle Love, and *Paranoia*

CLIVE BARKER

THE LIFE OF DEATH

Adapted by Fred Burke
Illustrated by Stewart Stanyard

AND

NEW MURDERS

ON THE RUE MORGUE

Adapted by Steve Niles
Illustrated by Hector Gomez

EclipseGraphicNovels
An Imprint of HarperCollins*Publishers*

Eclipse Graphic Novels
An Imprint of HarperCollins *Publishers*
77–85 Fulham Palace Road
Hammersmith, London W6 8JB

Published by Eclipse Graphic Novels 1993
9 8 7 6 5 4 3 2 1

The Life of Death Copyright © Clive Barker 1993
Adaptation Copyright © Fred Burke 1993
Artwork Copyright © Stewart Stanyard 1993

New Murders on the Rue Morgue
Copyright © Clive Barker 1993
Adaptation Copyright © Steve Niles 1993
Artwork Copyright © Hector Gomez 1993

The Author asserts the moral right to
be identified as the author of this work

ISBN 0 586 21758 4

Printed and bound in Hong Kong

THE NEWSPAPER WAS THE FIRST EDITION OF THE DAY, AND ELAINE DEVOURED IT FROM COVER TO COVER AS SHE SAT IN THE HOSPITAL WAITING ROOM.

An animal thought to be a panther—which had terrorized the neighborhood of Epping Forest for two months—had been shot and found to be a wild dog...
Archaeologists in the Sudan had discovered bone fragments which they opined might lead to a complete reappraisal of man's origins...
...A young woman who had once danced with minor royalty had been found murdered near Clapham...
...A solo round-the-world yachtsman was missing...
...Recently excited hopes of a cure for the common cold had been dashed.

SHE READ THE GLOBAL BULLETINS AND THE TRIVIA WITH EQUAL FERVOR--ANYTHING TO KEEP HER MIND OFF THE EXAMINATION AHEAD--BUT TODAY'S NEWS SEEMED VERY LIKE YESTERDAY'S.

ONLY THE NAMES HAD BEEN CHANGED.

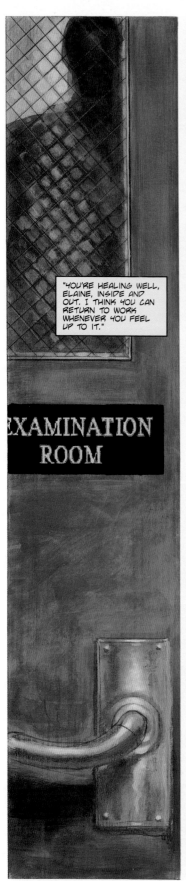

EXAMINATION
ROOM

"YOU'RE HEALING WELL, ELAINE, INSIDE AND OUT. I THINK YOU CAN RETURN TO WORK WHENEVER YOU FEEL UP TO IT."

MAKE ANOTHER APPOINTMENT FOR THE FIRST WEEK OF THE NEW YEAR. I'LL GIVE YOU A FINAL EXAMINATION THEN.

SHE LEFT HIM WASHING HIS HANDS OF HER.

THE THOUGHT OF GETTING STRAIGHT ONTO THE BUS AND HEADING BACK TO HER ROOMS WAS REPUGNANT AFTER SO MUCH TIME SITTING AND WAITING. SHE WOULD WALK A STOP OR TWO ALONG THE ROUTE, SHE DECIDED. THE EXERCISE WOULD BE GOOD FOR HER, AND THE DECEMBER DAY, THOUGH FAR FROM WARM, WAS BRIGHT.

HER PLANS PROVED OVERAMBITIOUS, HOWEVER.

AFTER ONLY A FEW MINUTES OF WALKING, HER LOWER ABDOMEN BEGAN TO ACHE, AND SHE STARTED TO FEEL NAUSEATED.

SHE TURNED OFF THE MAIN ROAD TO SEEK OUT A PLACE WHERE SHE COULD REST AND DRINK SOME TEA. SHE SHOULD EAT TOO, SHE KNEW, THOUGH SHE HAD NEVER HAD MUCH APPETITE, AND HAD LESS STILL SINCE THE OPERATION.

HER WANDERINGS WERE REWARDED. SHE FOUND A SMALL RESTAURANT WHICH, THOUGH IT WAS TWELVE FIFTY-FIVE, WAS NOT ENJOYING A ROARING LUNCHTIME TRADE.

A SMALL WOMAN WITH UNASHAMEDLY ARTIFICIAL RED HAIR TOOK HER ORDER: TEA AND A MUSHROOM OMELETTE.

S HE DID HER BEST TO EAT, BUT DIDN'T GET VERY FAR.

SOMETHING WRONG WITH THE FOOD?

OH NO. IT'S JUST ME.

I'D LIKE SOME MORE TEA THOUGH, IF I MAY?

T HE SIGHT OF THE MEAL CONGEALING ON THE PATTERNLESS PLATE WAS DOING NOTHING FOR HER MOOD. SHE HATED THIS UNWELCOME SENSITIVITY IN HERSELF: IT WAS ABSURD THAT A PLATE OF UNEATEN EGGS SHOULD BRING THESE DOLDRUMS ON, BUT SHE COULDN'T HELP HERSELF.

S HE FOUND EVERYWHERE LITTLE ECHOES OF HER OWN LOSS. IN THE DEATH, BY A BENIGN NOVEMBER AND THEN SUDDEN FROSTS, OF THE BULBS IN HER WINDOWSILL BOX, IN THE THOUGHT OF THE WILD DOG SHE'D READ OF THAT MORNING, SHOT IN EPPING FOREST.

MISS-- MY PLATE?

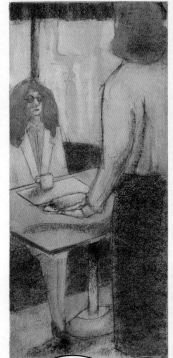

SHE IDLY WATCHED THE VEILS OF BLUE-GRAY SMOKE WHICH HAD CREPT DOWN THE STREET IN RECENT MINUTES, SOLIDIFYING THE SUNLIGHT.

THEY'RE BURNING AGAIN. DAMN SMELL GETS EVERY-WHERE.

WHAT ARE THEY BURNING?

USED TO BE THE COMMUNITY CENTER. THEY'RE KNOCKING IT DOWN AND BUILDING A NEW ONE. IT'S A WASTE OF TAXPAYER'S MONEY.

THE SMOKE WAS INDEED CREEPING INTO THE RESTAURANT. ELAINE DID NOT FIND IT OFFENSIVE; IT WAS SWEETLY REDOLENT OF AUTUMN, HER FAVORITE SEASON. INTRIGUED, SHE DECIDED TO WANDER ALONG AND FIND THE SOURCE OF THE SMOKE.

SHE DIDN'T HAVE FAR TO WALK. THERE
WAS ONE SURPRISE, HOWEVER. THE
BUILDING THAT THE WAITRESS HAD
DESCRIBED AS A COMMUNITY CENTER
WAS IN FACT A CHURCH, OR HAD BEEN.

THE INTERIOR, STRIPPED OF ITS DECORATIVE STONEWORK, OF PULPIT, PEWS, FONT AND THE REST, WAS SIMPLY A STONE ROOM, COMPLETELY LACKING IN ATMOSPHERE OR AUTHORITY.

SOMEBODY, HOWEVER, HAD FOUND A SOURCE OF INTEREST HERE.

OH! I WON'T BE A MOMENT.

THE MAN NODDED. HIS FEATURES, DESPITE THE GARB AND GRAY HAIRS OF A MAN IN MIDDLE AGE, WERE CURIOUSLY UNLINED, AS THOUGH NEITHER SMILE NOR FROWN MUCH RUFFLED THEIR PERFECT INDIFFERENCE.

SAD, ISN'T IT? SEEING A PLACE LIKE THIS.

DID YOU KNOW THE CHURCH AS IT USED TO BE?

IT'S ALL RIGHT--I THINK WE'RE PROBABLY BOTH TRESPASSING.

I CAME IN ON OCCASION, BUT IT WAS NEVER VERY POPULAR.

WHAT'S IT CALLED?

ALL SAINTS. IT WAS BUILT IN THE LATE SEVENTEENTH CENTURY, I BELIEVE. ARE YOU FOND OF CHURCHES?

NOT PARTICULARLY. IT WAS JUST THAT I SAW THE SMOKE, AND...

EVERYBODY LIKES A DEMOLITION SCENE.

YES, I SUPPOSE THAT'S TRUE.

IT'S LIKE WATCHING A FUNERAL. BETTER THEM THAN US, EH?

S HE MURMURED SOMETHING IN AGREEMENT, HER MIND FLITTING ELSEWHERE. BACK TO THE HOSPITAL, TO HER PAIN AND HER PRESENT HEALING, TO HER LIFE SAVED ONLY BY LOSING THE CAPACITY FOR FURTHER LIFE. BETTER THEM THAN US.

HE LEFT HER STANDING IN THE NAVE LIKE A FORSAKEN BRIDE, WHILE HE WENT OUT TO QUIZ ONE OF THE WORKMEN.

SHE WANDERED DOWN TO WHERE THE ALTAR HAD BEEN, READING THE NAMES AS SHE WENT.

WHO KNEW OR CARED ABOUT THESE PEOPLE'S RESTING PLACES NOW? DEAD TWO HUNDRED YEARS AND MORE, AND GONE AWAY NOT INTO LOVING POSTERITY BUT INTO OBLIVION.

AND SUDDENLY THE UNARTICULATED HOPES FOR AN AFTERLIFE SHE HAD NURSED THROUGH HER THIRTY-FOUR YEARS SLIPPED AWAY: SHE WAS NO LONGER WEIGHED DOWN BY SOME VAGUE AMBITION FOR HEAVEN.

ONE DAY, PERHAPS THIS DAY, SHE WOULD DIE, JUST AS THESE PEOPLE HAD DIED, AND IT WOULDN'T MATTER A JOT. THERE WAS NOTHING TO COME, NOTHING TO ASPIRE TO, NOTHING TO DREAM OF. SHE STOOD IN A PATCH OF SMOKE-THICKENED SUN, THINKING OF THIS, AND WAS ALMOST HAPPY.

THERE IS INDEED A CRYPT, BUT IT HASN'T BEEN EMPTIED YET.

STILL UNDERFOOT. DUST AND BONES.

APPARENTLY THEY'RE HAVING SOME DIFFICULTY GETTING INTO IT.

ALL THE ENTRANCES HAVE BEEN SEALED UP. THAT'S WHY THEY'RE DIGGING AROUND THE FOUNDATIONS. TO FIND ANOTHER WAY IN.

ARE CRYPTS NORMALLY SEALED UP?

NOT AS THOROUGHLY AS THIS ONE.

MAYBE THERE WAS NO MORE ROOM.

MAYBE.

WILL THEY GIVE YOU ONE OF THE STONES?

IT'S NOT UP TO THEM TO SAY. THESE ARE JUST COUNCIL LACKEYS.

APPARENTLY THEY HAVE A FIRM OF PROFESSIONAL EXCAVATORS TO COME IN AND SHIFT THE BODIES TO NEW BURIAL SITES. IT ALL HAS TO BE DONE WITH DUE DECORUM.

THEY TOLD ME TO COME BACK IN A DAY OR TWO'S TIME, AND ASK THE MOVING MEN.

SHE LAUGHED AT THE THOUGHT OF THE DEAD MOVING HOUSE, PACKING UP THEIR GOODS AND CHATTELS. KAVANAGH WAS PLEASED TO HAVE MADE A JOKE, EVEN IF IT HAD BEEN UNINTENTIONAL.

I WONDER, MAY I TAKE YOU FOR A DRINK?

I WOULDN'T BE VERY GOOD COMPANY, I'M AFRAID. I'M REALLY VERY TIRED--BEEN ILL RECENTLY

WE COULD PERHAPS MEET LATER...

HE WAS PLEASANT ENOUGH, IN HIS UNEVENTFUL WAY. SHE LIKED HIS GREEN BOW TIE--SURELY A JOKE AT THE EXPENSE OF HIS OWN DRABNESS. SHE LIKED HIS SERIOUSNESS TOO. BUT SHE COULDN'T FACE THE IDEA OF DRINKING WITH HIM, AT LEAST NOT TONIGHT.

I--I'M SORRY...

BEFORE THEY PARTED THEY EXCHANGED TELEPHONE NUMBERS. HE SEEMED CHARMINGLY EXCITED BY THE THOUGHT OF THEIR MEETING AGAIN; IT MADE HER FEEL, DESPITE ALL THAT HAD BEEN TAKEN FROM HER, THAT SHE STILL HAD HER SEX.

SHE RETURNED TO THE FLAT TO FIND BOTH A PARCEL FROM MITCH AND A HUNGRY CAT ON THE DOORSTEP. SHE FED THE DEMANDING ANIMAL, THEN MADE HERSELF SOME COFFEE AND OPENED THE PARCEL.

IN IT, COCOONED IN SEVERAL LAYERS OF TISSUE PAPER, SHE FOUND A SILK SCARF, CHOSEN WITH MITCH'S UNCANNY EYE FOR HER TASTE.

It's your color.
I love you.
Mitch

SHE WANTED TO PICK UP THE TELEPHONE ON THE SPOT AND TALK TO HIM, BUT SOMEHOW THE THOUGHT OF HEARING HIS VOICE SEEMED DANGEROUS. TOO CLOSE TO THE HURT, PERHAPS. HE WOULD ASK HER HOW SHE FELT, AND SHE WOULD REPLY THAT SHE WAS WELL, AND HE WOULD INSIST: YES, BUT *REALLY?*, AND SHE WOULD SAY: I'M EMPTY; THEY TOOK OUT HALF MY INNARDS, DAMN YOU, AND I'LL NEVER HAVE YOUR CHILDREN OR ANYBODY ELSE'S, SO THAT'S THE END OF THAT, ISN'T IT?

DAMN HIM FOR TRYING TO MAKE THINGS BETTER NOW, WHEN AT THE TIME SHE'D MOST NEEDED HIM ALL HE'D TALKED OF WAS FATHERHOOD--AND HOW HER TUMORS WOULD DENY IT HIM.

IT WAS A CLEAR EVENING--THE SKY'S COLD SKIN STRETCHED TO BREAKING POINT. SHE DID NOT WANT TO DRAW THE CURTAINS IN THE FRONT ROOM, EVEN THOUGH PASSERSBY WOULD STARE IN, BECAUSE THE DEEPENING BLUE WAS TOO FINE TO MISS.

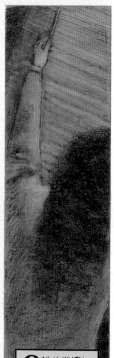

ONLY WHEN THE LAST CHANGE HAD BEEN WROUGHT DID SHE CLOSE OFF THE CHILL.

SHE HAD NO APPETITE, BUT SHE MADE HERSELF SOME FOOD NEVERTHELESS, AND SAT DOWN TO WATCH TELEVISION AS SHE ATE. THE FOOD UNFINISHED, SHE LAID DOWN HER TRAY AND DOZED, THE PROGRAMS FILTERING THROUGH TO HER INTERMITTENTLY...

...SOME WITLESS COMEDIAN WHOSE MEREST COUGH SENT HIS AUDIENCE INTO PAROXYSMS, A NATURAL HISTORY PROGRAM ON LIFE IN THE SERENGETI, THE NEWS.

SHE HAD READ ALL THAT SHE NEEDED TO KNOW THAT MORNING: THE HEADLINES HADN'T CHANGED.

ONE ITEM, HOWEVER, DID PIQUE HER CURIOSITY: AN INTERVIEW WITH THE SOLO YACHTSMAN, MICHAEL MAYBURY, WHO HAD BEEN PICKED UP THAT DAY AFTER TWO WEEKS ADRIFT IN THE PACIFIC.

THE INTERVIEW WAS BEING BEAMED FROM AUSTRALIA, AND THE CONTACT WAS BAD. THE PICTURE LITTLE MATTERED: THE ACCOUNT HE GAVE OF HIS FAILED VOYAGE WAS RIVETING IN SOUND ALONE, AND IN PARTICULAR AN EVENT THAT SEEMED TO DISTRESS HIM AFRESH EVEN AS HE TOLD IT.

HE HAD BEEN BECALMED, AND AS HIS VESSEL LACKED A MOTOR HAD BEEN OBLIGED TO WAIT FOR WIND. IT HAD NOT COME. A WEEK HAD GONE BY WITH HIS HARDLY MOVING A KILOMETER FROM THE SAME SPOT OF LISTLESS OCEAN; NO BIRD OR PASSING SHIP BROKE THE MONOTONY.

WITH EVERY HOUR THAT PASSED, HIS CLAUSTROPHOBIA GREW, AND ON THE EIGHTH DAY IT REACHED PANIC PROPORTIONS, SO HE LET HIMSELF OVER THE SIDE OF THE YACHT AND SWAM AWAY FROM THE VESSEL, A LIFELINE TIED ABOUT HIS MIDDLE, IN ORDER TO ESCAPE THE SAME FEW YARDS OF DECK.

BUT ONCE AWAY FROM THE YACHT, AND TREADING THE STILL, WARM WATER, HE HAD NO DESIRE TO GO BACK. WHY NOT UNTIE THE KNOT, HE'D THOUGHT TO HIMSELF, AND FLOAT AWAY...?

I DIDN'T DROWN. I COULD HAVE DIED THEN, IF I'D WANTED TO. SLIPPED OFF THE ROPE AND DROWNED.

BUT YOU DIDN'T. AND THE NEXT DAY--

THE NEXT DAY THE WIND PICKED UP.

"IT'S AN EXTRAORDI-NARY STORY. YOU MUST BE LOOKING FORWARD TO SEEING YOUR FAMILY AGAIN FOR CHRISTMAS"

ELAINE DIDN'T HEAR THE FINAL EXCHANGE OF PLEASANTRIES...

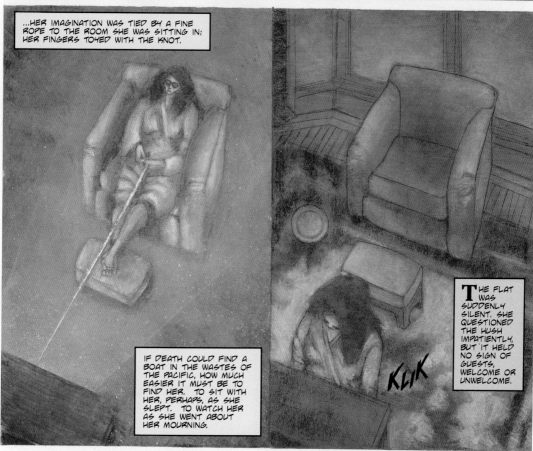

...HER IMAGINATION WAS TIED BY A FINE ROPE TO THE ROOM SHE WAS SITTING IN; HER FINGERS TOYED WITH THE KNOT.

IF DEATH COULD FIND A BOAT IN THE WASTES OF THE PACIFIC, HOW MUCH EASIER IT MUST BE TO FIND HER. TO SIT WITH HER, PERHAPS, AS SHE SLEPT. TO WATCH HER AS SHE WENT ABOUT HER MOURNING.

KLIK

THE FLAT WAS SUDDENLY SILENT. SHE QUESTIONED THE HUSH IMPATIENTLY, BUT IT HELD NO SIGN OF GUESTS, WELCOME OR UNWELCOME.

AS SHE LISTENED, SHE COULD TASTE SALT WATER.

OCEAN, NO DOUBT.

S HE HAD BEEN OFFERED SEVERAL REFUGES IN WHICH TO CONVALESCE WHEN SHE HAD FIRST COME OUT OF THE HOSPITAL. HER FATHER HAD INVITED HER UP TO ABERDEEN; HER SISTER RACHEL HAD MADE SEVERAL APPEALS FOR HER TO SPEND A FEW WEEKS IN BUCKINGHAMSHIRE; THERE HAD EVEN BEEN A PITIFUL TELEPHONE CALL FROM MITCH, IN WHICH HE HAD TALKED OF THEIR HOLIDAYING TOGETHER.

S HE HAD REJECTED THEM ALL, TELLING THEM THAT SHE WANTED TO REESTABLISH THE RHYTHM OF HER PREVIOUS LIFE AS SOON AS POSSIBLE: TO RETURN TO HER JOB, TO HER WORKING COLLEAGUES AND FRIENDS.

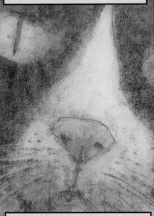

I N FACT, HER REASONS HAD GONE DEEPER THAN THAT. SHE HAD FEARED THEIR SYMPATHIES, FEARED THAT SHE WOULD BE HELD TOO CLOSE IN THEIR AFFECTIONS--

--AND QUICKLY COME TO RELY UPON THEM. HER STREAK OF INDEPENDENCE, WHICH HAD FIRST BROUGHT HER TO THIS UNFRIENDLY CITY, WAS IN STUDIED DEFIANCE OF HER SMOTHERING APPETITE FOR SECURITY. IF SHE GAVE IN TO THOSE LOVING APPEALS SHE KNEW SHE WOULD TAKE ROOT IN DOMESTIC SOIL AND NOT LOOK UP AND OUT AGAIN FOR ANOTHER YEAR. IN WHICH TIME, WHAT ADVENTURES MIGHT HAVE PASSED HER BY?

I NSTEAD SHE HAD RETURNED TO WORK AS SOON AS SHE FELT ABLE, HOPING THAT ALTHOUGH SHE HAD NOT TAKEN ON ALL HER FORMER RESPONSIBILITIES THE FAMILIAR ROUTINES WOULD HELP HER TO REESTABLISH A NORMAL LIFE.

B UT THE SLEIGHT OF HAND WAS NOT ENTIRELY SUCCESSFUL. EVERY FEW DAYS SOMETHING WOULD HAPPEN--SHE WOULD OVERHEAR SOME REMARK, OR CATCH A LOOK THAT SHE WAS NOT INTENDED TO SEE--

--THAT MADE HER REALIZE SHE WAS BEING TREATED WITH A REHEARSED CAUTION, THAT HER COLLEAGUES VIEWED HER AS BEING FUNDAMENTALLY CHANGED BY HER ILLNESS.

I T HAD MADE HER ANGRY. SHE'D WANTED TO SPIT HER SUSPICIONS IN THEIR FACES, TELL THEM THAT SHE AND HER UTERUS WERE NOT SYNONYMOUS, AND THAT THE REMOVAL OF ONE DID NOT IMPLY THE ECLIPSE OF THE OTHER.

BUT TODAY, RETURNING TO THE OFFICE, SHE WAS NOT SO CERTAIN THEY WEREN'T CORRECT. SHE FELT AS THOUGH SHE HADN'T SLEPT IN WEEKS, THOUGH IN FACT SHE WAS SLEEPING LONG AND DEEPLY EVERY NIGHT. HER EYESIGHT WAS BLURRED, AND THERE WAS A CURIOUS REMOTENESS ABOUT HER EXPERIENCES THAT DAY THAT SHE ASSOCIATED WITH EXTREME FATIGUE, AS IF SHE WERE DRIFTING FURTHER AND FURTHER FROM THE WORK ON HER DESK, FROM HER SENSATIONS, FROM HER VERY THOUGHTS.

TWICE THAT MORNING SHE CAUGHT HERSELF SPEAKING AND THEN WONDERED WHO IT WAS WHO WAS CONCEIVING OF THESE WORDS. IT CERTAINLY WASN'T HER; SHE WAS TOO BUSY LISTENING.

SHE HAD BEEN CALLED INTO HER SUPERVISOR'S OFFICE AND SPED TO SIT DOWN...

ARE YOU ALL RIGHT, ELAINE?

YES. I'M FINE.

THERE'S BEEN SOME CONCERN--

ABOUT WHAT?

YOUR BEHAVIOR. PLEASE DON'T THINK I'M PRYING, ELAINE. IT'S JUST THAT IF YOU NEED SOME FURTHER TIME TO RECUPERATE--

THERE'S NOTHING WRONG WITH ME.

BUT YOUR WEEPING--

WHAT?

THE WAY YOU'VE BEEN CRYING TODAY. IT CONCERNS US.

CRY? I DON'T CRY.

BUT YOU'VE BEEN CRYING ALL DAY. YOU'RE CRYING NOW.

I DIDN'T...I DIDN'T KNOW.

THOUGH THE WORDS SOUNDED PREPOSTEROUS, THEY WERE TRUE. SHE HADN'T KNOWN. ONLY NOW, WITH THE FACT POINTED OUT, DID SHE TASTE TEARS IN HER THROAT AND SINUSES AND HER MEMORY RETURNED TO THE OCEAN OF THE NIGHT BEFORE.

WHY DON'T YOU TAKE THE REST OF THE DAY OFF?

YES.

TAKE THE REST OF THE WEEK, IF YOU'D LIKE. YOU'RE A VALUED MEMBER OF STAFF, ELAINE; I DON'T HAVE TO TELL YOU THAT. WE DON'T WANT YOU COMING TO ANY HARM.

THIS LAST REMARK STRUCK HOME WITH STINGING FORCE. DID THEY THINK SHE WAS VERGING ON SUICIDE? WAS THAT WHY SHE WAS TREATED WITH KID GLOVES? THEY WERE ONLY TEARS SHE WAS SHEDDING, FOR GOD'S SAKE, AND SHE WAS SO INDIFFERENT TO THEM SHE HAD NOT EVEN KNOWN THEY WERE FALLING.

I'LL GO HOME. THANK YOU FOR YOUR... CONCERN.

IT MUST HAVE BEEN A VERY TRAUMATIC EXPERIENCE. WE ALL UNDERSTAND, WE REALLY DO. IF YOU FEEL YOU WANT TO TALK ABOUT IT AT ANY TIME--

NO-- BUT THANK YOU.

FACE-TO-FACE WITH HERSELF IN THE MIRROR OF THE WOMAN'S TOILETS SHE REALIZED JUST HOW BAD SHE LOOKED. HER SKIN WAS FLUSHED, HER EYES SWOLLEN. SHE DID WHAT SHE COULD TO CONCEAL THE SIGNS OF THIS PAINLESS GRIEF, THEN PICKED UP HER COAT AND STARTED HOME.

SHE KNEW RETURNING TO THE EMPTY FLAT WOULD NOT BE A WISE IDEA. SHE WOULD BROOD, SHE WOULD SLEEP (SO MUCH SLEEP OF LATE, AND SO PERFECTLY DREAMLESS), BUT SHE WOULD NOT IMPROVE HER MENTAL CONDITION BY EITHER ROUTE.

A NEARBY CHURCH BELL, TOLLING THE CLEAR AFTERNOON, REMINDED HER OF THE SMOKE AND THE SQUARE AND MISTER KAVANAGH. THERE, SHE DECIDED, WAS A FIT PLACE FOR HER TO WALK. SHE COULD ENJOY THE SUNLIGHT, AND THINK. MAYBE SHE WOULD MEET HER ADMIRER AGAIN.

SHE FOUND HER WAY BACK TO ALL SAINTS EASILY ENOUGH, BUT THERE WAS DISAPPOINTMENT AWAITING HER. THE WORKERS AND THEIR HAMMERS HAD BEEN EXILED FROM THE SHADOWS OF ALL SAINTS AND NOW A VERY DIFFERENT SELECTION OF PEOPLE--SUITED AND ACADEMIC-- OCCUPIED THE ZONE BEYOND THE RIBBON, SOME IN FURROWED CONVERSATION, OTHERS STANDING ON THE MUDDY GROUND AND STARING UP QUIZZICALLY AT THE DERELICT CHURCH.

OCCASIONALLY SOMEBODY WOULD EMERGE FROM BEHIND THIS VEIL AND CONSULT WITH OTHERS ON THE SITE.

ALL WHO DID SO, SHE NOTED, WERE WEARING GLOVES; ONE OR TWO WERE ALSO MASKED. IT WAS AS THOUGH THEY WERE PERFORMING SOME AD HOC SURGERY IN THE SHELTER OF THE SCREEN. A TUMOR, PERHAPS, IN THE BOWELS OF ALL SAINTS.

WHAT'S GOING ON?

THE FOUNDATIONS ARE UNSTABLE. APPARENTLY THE PLACE COULD FALL DOWN AT ANY MOMENT.

WHY ARE THEY WEARING MASKS?

IT'S JUST A PRECAUTION AGAINST THE DUST.

S HE DIDN'T ARGUE, THOUGH THIS EXPLANATION STRUCK HER AS UNLIKELY.

IF YOU WANT TO GET THROUGH TO TEMPLE STREET YOU'LL HAVE TO GO ROUND THE BACK.

MISTER KAVANAGH!

A S SHE BEGAN TO MAKE HER WAY BACK TO THE MAIN ROAD SHE CAUGHT SIGHT OF A FAMILIAR FIGURE CROSSING THE END OF AN ADJACENT STREET.

WELL, WELL. I DIDN'T EXPECT TO SEE YOU AGAIN SO SOON.

I'M SO PLEASED. DO YOU WANT TO HAVE SOME AFTERNOON TEA? THERE'S A PLACE JUST DOWN THE STREET.

IT'S THE CRYPT.

THEY'VE OPENED IT?

I WAS HERE THIS MORNING--

ABOUT YOUR STONES?

SOME OF THEM WERE WEARING MASKS.

IT WON'T SMELL VERY FRESH DOWN THERE. NOT AFTER SO LONG.

I WONDER WHAT IT'S LIKE.

I CAME TO WATCH THE REST OF THE DEMO-LITION.

I'D LIKE THAT.

THEY CERTAINLY FOUND A WAY IN.

THAT'S RIGHT. THEY WERE ALREADY PUTTING UP THE TARPAULINS THEN.

A WONDERLAND.

A WONDERLAND, YES.

I LIKE PLACES WHERE THE DEAD ARE. I ALWAYS HAVE. CEMETERIES CAN BE VERY BEAUTIFUL, DON'T YOU THINK? MAUSOLEUMS AND TOMBS, ALL THE FINE CRAFTSMANSHIP THAT GOES INTO THOSE PLACES. EVEN THE DEAD MAY SOMETIMES REWARD CLOSER SCRUTINY.

THEY CAN BE VERY BEAUTIFUL ON OCCASION. IT'S SORT OF A GLAMOUR THEY HAVE. IT'S A SHAME IT'S WASTED ON MORTICIANS AND FUNERAL DIRECTORS.

I'M SURE THERE'S MUCH TO BE SEEN IN THAT CRYPT. STRANGE SIGHTS. WONDERFUL SIGHTS.

I ONLY EVER SAW ONE DEAD PERSON. MY GRANDMOTHER. I WAS VERY YOUNG AT THE TIME...

I TRUST IT WAS A PIVOTAL EXPERIENCE.

I DON'T THINK SO. IN FACT I SCARCELY REMEMBER IT AT ALL. I ONLY REMEMBER HOW EVERYBODY CRIED.

SO SELFISH. DON'T YOU THINK? SPOILING A FAREWELL WITH SNOT AND SOBS. WE CRY FOR OURSELVES, DON'T WE?

NOT FOR THE DEAD. THE DEAD ARE PAST CARING.

YES. MY GOD, YES. THAT'S RIGHT. ALWAYS FOR OURSELVES...

YOU SEE HOW MUCH THE DEAD CAN TEACH, JUST BY LYING THERE TWIDDLING THEIR THUMB BONES?

SHE HAD MISJUDGED HIM ON THAT INITIAL MEETING, THINKING HIS FACE UNUSED TO SMILES; IT WAS NOT, AS A FURTHER HALF HOUR OF HIS LACONIC REMARKS AMPLY PROVED. BUT HIS FEATURES, WHENEVER THE LAUGHTER DIED, SWIFTLY REGAINED THAT EERIE QUIESCENCE SHE HAD FIRST NOTICED.

WELL, THANK YOU FOR A LOVELY AFTERNOON. NOBODY'S MADE ME LAUGH SO MUCH IN WEEKS. I'M GRATEFUL.

YOU SHOULD LAUGH. IT SUITS YOU. YOU HAVE BEAUTIFUL TEETH.

HE WAS UNDOUBTEDLY ONE OF THE MOST OFFBEAT INDIVIDUALS SHE'D EVER ENCOUNTERED, BUT HE HAD COME INTO HER LIFE--WITH HIS EAGERNESS TO TALK OF CRYPTS AND THE DEAD AND THE BEAUTY OF HER TEETH--AT JUST THE RIGHT MOMENT.

ON THE JOURNEY BACK, AND LATER THAT EVENING, SHE THOUGHT PARTICULARLY OF THE JOKE HE HAD MADE ABOUT THE DEAD TWIDDLING THEIR THUMB BONES, AND THAT THOUGHT LED INEVITABLY TO THE MYSTERIES THAT LAY OUT OF SIGHT IN THE CRYPT.

SHE BADLY WANTED TO SLIP THROUGH THAT CORDON OF RIBBON AND SEE THE BURIAL CHAMBER WITH HER OWN EYES. IT WAS A DESIRE SHE WOULD NEVER PREVIOUSLY HAVE ADMITTED TO HERSELF.

BUT KAVANAGH HAD LEGITIMIZED HER APPETITE WITH HIS FLAGRANT ENTHUSIASM FOR THINGS FUNEREAL.

NOW, WITH THE TABOO SHED, SHE WANTED TO GO BACK TO ALL SAINTS AND LOOK DEATH IN ITS FACE; THEN NEXT TIME SHE SAW KAVANAGH SHE WOULD HAVE SOME STORIES TO TELL OF HER OWN.

SHE WATCHED IN SILENCE AS THE SHIVERING POLICEMEN TOOK SHELTER, TURNING ON A RADIO IN THE WORKMEN'S HUT...

...ITS NOISE (MUSIC FOR LOVERS FROM DUSK TO DAWN, THE DISTANT VOICE PURRED) WOULD COVER HER CRACKLING ADVANCE ACROSS THE FROZEN EARTH.

BEHIND HER, THE MUSIC FOR LOVERS MURMURED ON. NO ONE EMERGED FROM THE HUT TO SUMMON HER FROM HER TRESPASSING. NO ALARM BELLS RANG.

THE DEMOLITION MEN, UNDER VERY SPECIFIC INSTRUCTIONS TO JUDGE BY THE CARE THEY HAD TAKEN IN THEIR LABORS, HAD DUG FULLY EIGHT FEET DOWN THE SIDE OF ALL SAINTS, EXPOSING THE FOUNDATIONS. IN SO DOING THEY HAD UNCOVERED AN ENTRANCE TO THE BURIAL CHAMBER THAT PREVIOUS HANDS HAD BEEN AT PAINS TO CONCEAL.

NOT ONLY HAD EARTH BEEN PILED UP AGAINST THE FLANK OF THE CHURCH TO HIDE THE ENTRANCE, BUT ALSO THE CRYPT DOOR HAD BEEN REMOVED, AND STONE MASONS SEALED THE ENTIRE APERTURE UP. THIS HAD CLEARLY BEEN DONE AT SOME SPEED; THEIR HANDIWORK WAS FAR FROM ORDERED. THEY HAD SIMPLY FILLED THE ENTRANCE UP WITH ANY STONE OR BRICK THAT HAD COME TO HAND, AND PLASTERED COARSE MORTAR OVER THEIR ENDEAVORS. INTO THIS MORTAR--THOUGH THE DESIGN HAD BEEN SPOILED BY THE EXCAVATIONS--SOME ARTISAN HAD SCRAWLED A SIX-FOOT CROSS.

ALL THEIR EFFORTS IN SECURING THE CRYPT, AND MARKING THE MORTAR TO KEEP THE GODLESS OUT, HAD GONE FOR NOTHING, HOWEVER.

THE SEAL HAD BEEN BROKEN-- THE MORTAR HACKED AT, THE STONES TORN AWAY. THERE WAS NOW A SMALL HOLE IN THE MIDDLE OF THE DOORWAY, LARGE ENOUGH FOR ONE PERSON TO GAIN ACCESS TO THE INTERIOR. ELAINE HAD NO HESITATION IN CLIMBING DOWN THE SLOPE TO THE BREACHED WALL, AND THEN SQUIRMING THROUGH.

SHE HAD PREDICTED THE DARKNESS SHE MET ON THE OTHER SIDE, AND HAD BROUGHT WITH HER A CIGARETTE LIGHTER MITCH HAD GIVEN HER THREE YEARS AGO.

IT WAS NOT THE CRYPT ITSELF SHE HAD STEPPED INTO BUT A NARROW VESTIBULE OF SOME KIND: A YARD OR SO IN FRONT OF HER WAS ANOTHER WALL, AND ANOTHER DOOR.

THE LOCK HAD BEEN REMOVED-- BY THE INVESTIGATORS PRESUMABLY--AND THE DOOR THEN HELD SHUT AGAIN WITH A ROPE BINDING. THIS HAD BEEN DONE QUICKLY, BY TIRED FINGERS.

SHE DID NOT FIND THE ROPE DIFFICULT TO UNTIE, THOUGH IT REQUIRED BOTH HANDS, AND SO HAD TO BE EFFECTED IN THE DARK.

AS SHE WORKED THE KNOT FREE, SHE HEARD VOICES. THE POLICEMEN-- DAMN THEM--HAD LEFT THE SECLUSION OF THEIR HUT AND COME OUT INTO THE BITTER NIGHT TO DO THEIR ROUNDS.

THE OFFICERS' VOICES WERE BECOMING LOUDER: TALKING OF THEIR CHILDREN, AND THE ESCALATING COST OF CHRISTMAS JOY. NOW THEY WERE WITHIN YARDS OF THE CRYPT ENTRANCE, STANDING, OR SO SHE GUESSED, IN THE SHELTER OF THE TARPAULIN

THEY MADE NO ATTEMPT TO DESCEND THE SLOPE, HOWEVER, BUT FINISHED THEIR CURSORY INSPECTION ON THE LIP OF THE EARTHWORKS, THEN TURNED BACK. THEIR VOICES FADED.

SO THIS WAS DEATH. THERE WAS NONE OF THE ART OR THE GLAMOUR KAVANAGH HAD TALKED OF, NO CALM LAYING OUT OF SHROUDED BEAUTIES ON COOL MARBLE SHEETS, NO ELABORATE RELIQUARIES, NOR APHORISMS ON THE NATURE OF HUMAN FRAILTY: NOT EVEN NAMES AND DATES. IN MOST CASES, THE CORPSES LACKED EVEN COFFINS.

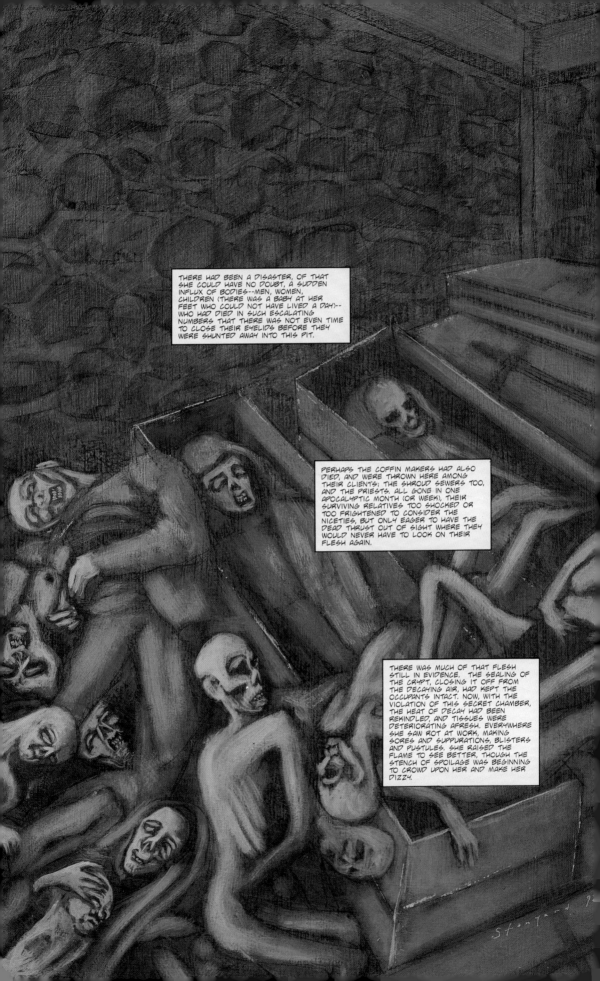

THERE HAD BEEN A DISASTER, OF THAT SHE COULD HAVE NO DOUBT, A SUDDEN INFLUX OF BODIES--MEN, WOMEN, CHILDREN (THERE WAS A BABY AT HER FEET WHO COULD NOT HAVE LIVED A DAY)-- WHO HAD DIED IN SUCH ESCALATING NUMBERS THAT THERE WAS NOT EVEN TIME TO CLOSE THEIR EYELIDS BEFORE THEY WERE SHUNTED AWAY INTO THIS PIT.

PERHAPS THE COFFIN MAKERS HAD ALSO DIED, AND WERE THROWN HERE AMONG THEIR CLIENTS; THE SHROUD SEWERS TOO, AND THE PRIESTS, ALL GONE IN ONE APOCALYPTIC MONTH (OR WEEK), THEIR SURVIVING RELATIVES TOO SHOCKED OR TOO FRIGHTENED TO CONSIDER THE NICETIES, BUT ONLY EAGER TO HAVE THE DEAD THRUST OUT OF SIGHT WHERE THEY WOULD NEVER HAVE TO LOOK ON THEIR FLESH AGAIN.

THERE WAS MUCH OF THAT FLESH STILL IN EVIDENCE. THE SEALING OF THE CRYPT, CLOSING IT OFF FROM THE DECAYING AIR, HAD KEPT THE OCCUPANTS INTACT. NOW, WITH THE VIOLATION OF THIS SECRET CHAMBER, THE HEAT OF DECAY HAD BEEN REKINDLED, AND TISSUES WERE DETERIORATING AFRESH. EVERYWHERE SHE SAW ROT AT WORK, MAKING SORES AND SUPPURATIONS, BLISTERS AND PUSTULES. SHE RAISED THE FLAME TO SEE BETTER, THOUGH THE STENCH OF SPOILAGE WAS BEGINNING TO CROWD UPON HER AND MAKE HER DIZZY.

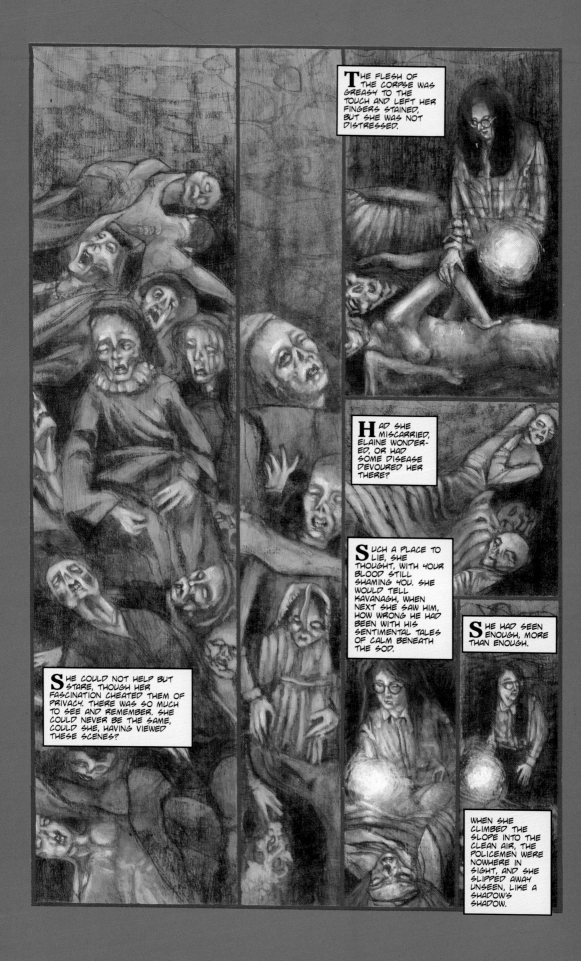

THE FLESH OF THE CORPSE WAS GREASY TO THE TOUCH AND LEFT HER FINGERS STAINED, BUT SHE WAS NOT DISTRESSED.

HAD SHE MISCARRIED, ELAINE WONDERED, OR HAD SOME DISEASE DEVOURED HER THERE?

SUCH A PLACE TO LIE, SHE THOUGHT, WITH YOUR BLOOD STILL SHAMING YOU. SHE WOULD TELL KAVANAGH, WHEN NEXT SHE SAW HIM, HOW WRONG HE HAD BEEN WITH HIS SENTIMENTAL TALES OF CALM BENEATH THE SOD.

SHE HAD SEEN ENOUGH, MORE THAN ENOUGH.

SHE COULD NOT HELP BUT STARE, THOUGH HER FASCINATION CHEATED THEM OF PRIVACY. THERE WAS SO MUCH TO SEE AND REMEMBER. SHE COULD NEVER BE THE SAME, COULD SHE, HAVING VIEWED THESE SCENES?

WHEN SHE CLIMBED THE SLOPE INTO THE CLEAN AIR, THE POLICEMEN WERE NOWHERE IN SIGHT, AND SHE SLIPPED AWAY UNSEEN, LIKE A SHADOW'S SHADOW.

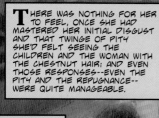

THERE WAS NOTHING FOR HER TO FEEL, ONCE SHE HAD MASTERED HER INITIAL DISGUST AND THAT TWINGE OF PITY SHE'D FELT SEEING THE CHILDREN AND THE WOMAN WITH THE CHESTNUT HAIR; AND EVEN THOSE RESPONSES--EVEN THE PITY AND THE REPUGNANCE--WERE QUITE MANAGEABLE.

SHE HAD FELT BOTH MORE ACUTELY SEEING A DOG RUN DOWN BY A CAR THAN SHE HAD STANDING IN THE CRYPT OF ALL SAINTS, DESPITE THE HORRID DISPLAYS ON EVERY SIDE.

WHEN SHE LAY HER HEAD DOWN TO SLEEP THAT NIGHT, AND REALIZED THAT SHE WAS NEITHER TREMBLING NOR NAUSEATED, SHE FELT STRONG.

WHAT WAS THERE TO FEAR IN ALL THE WORLD IF THE SPECTACLE OF MORTALITY SHE HAD JUST WITNESSED COULD BE BORNE SO READILY? SHE SLEPT DEEPLY, AND WOKE REFRESHED.

I'M SORRY I BEHAVED SO POORLY YESTERDAY. I'M FEELING MUCH BETTER TODAY--REALLY. BETTER THAN I'VE FELT IN MONTHS

SHE COULD SENSE HER COLLEAGUES DOUBTING THAT THIS BOUT OF SUNSHINE ACTUALLY MEANT A SUMMER.

BUT WHEN THE MOOD WAS SUSTAINED THROUGHOUT THE DAY AND THROUGH THE DAY FOLLOWING, THEY BEGAN TO RESPOND MORE READILY. BY THURSDAY IT WAS AS THOUGH THE TEARS OF EARLIER IN THE WEEK HAD NEVER BEEN SHED.

YOU'RE LOOKING SO WELL, ELAINE!

IT WAS TRUE: HER EYES SHONE, SKIN SHONE. SHE WAS A PICTURE OF VITALITY.

So much to do, so many wasted, grieving days to catch up on. An apt phrase flitted into her head. *Redeem the time.*

Where did the words come from? She couldn't recall.

It didn't matter. Sometimes there was wisdom in forgetting.

WELL, HELLO!

I THOUGHT I'D RING YOU UP-- SEE IF YOU MIGHT BE FREE FOR DINNER TOMORROW.

"OH, THAT WOULD BE WONDERFUL-- BUT MY FRIEND REUBEN IS THROWING ME A PARTY, SOMETHING TO CELEBRATE MY RETURN TO HEALTH. MIGHT YOU COME?"

THANKS, BUT-- WELL, LARGE NUMBERS OF PEOPLE HAVE ALWAYS INTIMIDATED ME.

DON'T BE FOOLISH--EVERYONE WOULD BE PLEASED TO MEET YOU. BESIDES, I'D LIKE THE CHANCE TO SHOW YOU OFF.

DINNER'S AT SEVEN P.M.--WIMPOLE STREET, NUMBER 36.

"WELL I'LL TRY-- BUT ONLY IF MY EGO FEELS UP TO IT. YOU WON'T BE OFFENDED IF I DON'T MAKE IT, WILL YOU?"

WHAT NONSENSE-- OF COURSE NOT! BUT YOU REALLY SHOULD COME. NEXT TIME I SEE YOU, I'VE GOT QUITE A TALE TO TELL.

THE FOLLOWING DAY BROUGHT UNHAPPY NEWS. BERNICE HAD DIED IN THE EARLY HOURS OF FRIDAY MORNING, WITHOUT EVER REGAINING CONSCIOUSNESS. THE CAUSE OF DEATH WAS AS YET UNVERIFIED, BUT THE OFFICE GOSSIPS CONCURRED THAT SHE HAD NEVER BEEN A STRONG WOMAN--ALWAYS THE FIRST AMONG THE SECRETARIES TO CATCH A COLD AND THE LAST TO SHAKE IT OFF.

THERE WAS ALSO SOME TALK, THOUGH TRADED LESS LOUDLY, ABOUT HER PERSONAL BEHAVIOR. SHE HAD BEEN GENEROUS WITH HER FAVORS IT APPEARED, AND INJUDICIOUS IN HER CHOICE OF PARTNERS. WITH VENEREAL DISEASES REACHING EPIDEMIC PROPORTIONS, WAS THAT NOT THE LIKELIEST EXPLANATION FOR THE DEATH?

THE NEWS, THOUGH IT KEPT THE RUMORMONGERS IN BUSINESS, WAS NOT GOOD FOR GENERAL MORALE. TWO GIRLS WENT SICK THAT MORNING, AND IT SEEMED AT LUNCHTIME THAT ELAINE WAS THE ONLY MEMBER OF STAFF WITH AN APPETITE.

SHE COMPENSATED FOR THE LACK IN HER COLLEAGUES, HOWEVER. SHE HAD A FIERCE HUNGER IN HER; HER BODY ALMOST SEEMED TO ACHE FOR SUSTENANCE. IT WAS A GOOD FEELING AFTER SO MANY MONTHS OF LASSITUDE.

WHEN SHE LOOKED AROUND AT THE WORN FACES AT THE TABLE SHE FELT UTTERLY APART FROM THEM--

--FROM THEIR TITTLE-TATTLE AND THEIR TRIVIAL OPINIONS, FROM THE WAY THEIR TALK CIRCLED ON THE SUDDENNESS OF BERNICE'S DEATH AS THOUGH THEY HAD NOT GIVEN THE SUBJECT A MOMENT'S THOUGHT IN YEARS, AND WERE AMAZED THAT THEIR NEGLECT HAD NOT RENDERED IT EXTINCT.

ELAINE KNEW BETTER. SHE HAD COME CLOSE TO DEATH SO OFTEN IN THE RECENT PAST--

--DURING THE MONTHS LEADING UP TO HER HYSTERECTOMY, WHEN THE TUMORS HAD SUDDENLY DOUBLED IN SIZE AS THOUGH SENSING THAT THEY WERE PLOTTED AGAINST; ON THE OPERATING TABLE, WHEN TWICE THE SURGEONS THOUGHT THEY'D LOST HER; AND MOST RECENTLY, IN THE CRYPT, FACE-TO-FACE WITH THOSE GAWPING CARCASSES.

DEATH WAS EVERYWHERE. THAT THEY SHOULD BE SO STARTLED BY ITS ENTRANCES INTO THEIR CHARMLESS CIRCLE STRUCK HER AS ALMOST COMICAL.

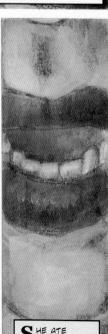

SHE ATE LUSTILY, AND LET THEM TALK IN WHISPERS.

THEY GATHERED FOR HER PARTY AT REUBEN'S HOUSE-- ELAINE, HERMIONE, SAM AND NELLWYN, JOSH AND SONJA. IT WAS A GOOD NIGHT, A CHANCE TO PICK UP ON HOW MUTUAL FRIENDS WERE FARING, HOW STATUSES AND AMBITIONS WERE ON THE CHANGE.

MAYBURY? WHAT ABOUT HIM?

SAM AND I WERE JUST SAYING HOW STRANGE IT ALL WAS--

I SAW HIM ON THE NEWS.

SAD STORY, ISN'T IT? THE WAY IT HAPPENED.

WHY SAD?

HIM SAYING THAT-- ABOUT DEATH BEING ON THE BOAT WITH HIM--AND THEN DYING.

EVERYONE GOT DRUNK VERY QUICKLY; TONGUES ALREADY LOOSENED BY FAMILIARITY BECAME PROGRESSIVELY LOOSER. NELLWYN LED A TEARFUL TOAST TO ELAINE; JOSH AND SONJA HAD A SHORT BUT ACRIMONIOUS EXCHANGE ON THE SUBJECT OF EVANGELISM; REUBEN DID HIS IMPERSONATIONS OF FELLOW BARRISTERS.

IT WAS LIKE OLD TIMES, EXCEPT THAT MEMORY HAD YET TO IMPROVE IT. KAVANAGH DID NOT PUT IN AN APPEARANCE, AND ELAINE WAS GLAD OF IT DESPITE HER PROTES- TATIONS WHEN SPEAKING TO HIM. SHE KNEW HE WOULD HAVE FELT OUT OF PLACE IN SUCH CLOSE- KNIT COMPANY.

SO SAD.

DYING? WHEN WAS THIS?

IT WAS IN ALL THE PAPERS.

HE WAS KILLED. THEY WERE TAKING HIM TO THE AIRPORT TO FLY HIM HOME, AND THERE WAS AN ACCIDENT. HE WAS KILLED JUST LIKE THAT. OUT LIKE A LIGHT.

HERMIONE GLANCED AT ELAINE, AND A FROWN CREPT ACROSS HER FACE.

THE LOOK BAFFLED ELAINE UNTIL--

--WITH THAT SAME SHOCK OF RECOGNITION SHE'D FELT IN CHIMES'S OFFICE, DISCOVERING HER TEARS--SHE REALIZED THAT SHE WAS SMILING.

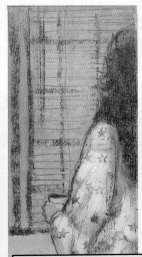

THE FIRST SNOW OF WINTER WAS IN THE WIND, THOUGH IT WAS TOO WET TO MAKE ANY SERIOUS IMPRESSION ON THE STREETS. THE CHILL WAS BITING ENOUGH, HOWEVER, TO JUDGE BY THE SCOWLS ON THE FACES OF PASSERSBY. SHE FELT ODDLY IMMUNE FROM IT, HOWEVER, AS THOUGH SHE HAD A FIRE STOKED IN HER BELLY.

SHE WOKE UP LATE ON SATURDAY MORNING, WITHOUT THE ANTICIPATED HANGOVER. THERE WAS A LETTER FROM MITCH. SHE DIDN'T OPEN IT, BUT LEFT IT FOR AN IDLE MOMENT LATER IN THE DAY.

SINCE THE REMOVAL OF THE DRESSINGS SHE HAD STUDIOUSLY AVOIDED ANY CLOSE SCRUTINY OF HER BODY, BUT TODAY HER QUALMS AND HER VANITY SEEMED TO HAVE DISAPPEARED.

SHE WAS PLEASED WITH WHAT SHE SAW. THE SCAR ITSELF STILL LOOKED AND FELT TENDER, BUT HER EYES READ ITS LIVIDNESS AS A SIGN OF HER CUNT'S AMBITION, AS THOUGH ANY DAY NOW HER SEX WOULD GROW FROM ANUS TO NAVEL (AND BEYOND PERHAPS), OPENING HER UP, MAKING HER TERRIBLE.

IT WAS PARADOXICAL, SURELY, THAT IT WAS ONLY NOW, WHEN THE SURGEONS HAD EMPTIED HER OUT, THAT SHE SHOULD FEEL SO RIPE, SO RESPLENDENT. SHE STOOD FOR FULLY HALF AN HOUR IN FRONT OF THE MIRROR ADMIRING HERSELF, HER THOUGHTS DRIFTING OFF.

IT WAS TIME SHE FOUND HERSELF SOMETHING TO EAT; SHE HAD THAT FAMILIAR FIERCE HUNGER UPON HER.

THE FRIDGE WAS PRACTICALLY EMPTY. SHE WOULD HAVE TO GO OUT AND STOCK UP FOR THE WEEKEND.

THE SNOW HAD THICKENED. THROUGH THE FLURRIES SHE CAUGHT A MOVEMENT IN THE ALLEY BETWEEN THE HOUSES OPPOSITE. SOMEBODY WAS THERE, WATCHING HER, THOUGH SHE COULDN'T SEE WHO.

SHE DIDN'T MIND. SHE STOOD PEEPING AT THE PEEPER, WONDERING IF HE WOULD HAVE THE COURAGE TO SHOW HIMSELF, BUT HE DID NOT. SHE WATCHED FOR SEVERAL MINUTES BEFORE SHE REALIZED THAT HER BRAZENNESS HAD FRIGHTENED HIM AWAY.

SUPERMARKETS WERE CIRCUSES, ESPECIALLY ON A SATURDAY, BUT HER MOOD WAS FAR TOO BUOYANT TO BE DEPRESSED BY HAVING TO MAKE HER WAY THROUGH THE CROWDS.

TODAY SHE EVEN FOUND SOME PLEASURE IN THESE SCENES OF CONSPICUOUS CONSUMPTION: IN THE SHOPPING CARTS AND THE BASKETS HEAPED HIGH WITH FOODSTUFFS, AND THE CHILDREN GREEDY EYED AS THEY APPROACHED THE CONFECTIONARY AND TEARFUL IF DENIED IT, AND THE WIVES WEIGHING UP THE MERITS OF A LEG OF MUTTON WHILE THEIR HUSBANDS WATCHED THE GIRLS ON THE STAFF WITH EYES NO LESS CALCULATING.

SHE PURCHASED TWICE AS MUCH FOOD FOR THE WEEKEND AS SHE WOULD NORMALLY HAVE DONE IN A FULL WEEK, HER APPETITE DRIVEN TO DISTRACTION BY THE SMELLS FROM THE DELICATESSEN AND FRESH-MEAT COUNTERS.

BY THE TIME SHE REACHED THE HOUSE SHE WAS ALMOST SHAKING WITH THE ANTICIPATION OF SUSTENANCE.

ELAINE?

ARE YOU FEELING ALL RIGHT?

THE POINT IS--ARE YOU?

YES, I'M FINE. WHY SHOULDN'T I BE?

SONJA'S GONE DOWN WITH SOME KIND OF FOOD POISONING, AND SO'S REUBEN. I JUST CAME ROUND TO SEE THAT YOU WERE ALL RIGHT.

AS I SAY, FINE.

I DON'T UNDERSTAND IT. THEY'VE TAKEN REUBEN INTO THE HOSPITAL FOR TESTS, AND I'VE HAD NO LUCK GETTING AHOLD OF NELLWYN AND SAM.

DO YOU WANT TO COME IN AND HAVE A CUP OF COFFEE?

NO, THANKS, I'VE GOT TO GET BACK TO SEE SONJA. I JUST DIDN'T LIKE TO THINK OF YOUR BEING ON YOUR OWN IF YOU'D GONE DOWN WITH IT TOO.

YOU'RE AN ANGEL.

I MUST... I MUST GO.

I'LL CALL YOU LATER IN THE DAY AND FIND OUT HOW THEY'RE DOING.

AS SHE SET TO DEVOURING THE GROCERIES, ELAINE THOUGHT OF THE PALTRY OMELETTE SHE'D BEEN UNABLE TO FINISH THAT DAY AFTER THE VISIT TO THE HOSPITAL.

ONE THOUGHT LED TO ANOTHER--

--FROM OMELETTE TO SMOKE TO THE SQUARE TO KAVANAGH TO HER MOST RECENT VISIT TO THE CHURCH, AND THINKING OF THE PLACE SHE WAS SUDDENLY SEIZED BY AN ENTHUSIASM TO SEE IT ONE FINAL TIME BEFORE IT WAS ENTIRELY LEVELED.

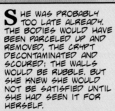

SHE WAS PROBABLY TOO LATE ALREADY. THE BODIES WOULD HAVE BEEN PARCELED UP AND REMOVED, THE CRYPT DECONTAMINATED AND SCOURED; THE WALLS WOULD BE RUBBLE. BUT SHE KNEW SHE WOULD NOT BE SATISFIED UNTIL SHE HAD SEEN IT FOR HERSELF.

EVEN AFTER A MEAL WHICH WOULD HAVE SICKENED HER WITH ITS EXCESS A FEW DAYS BEFORE, SHE FELT LIGHT-HEADED AS SHE SET OUT FOR ALL SAINTS, ALMOST AS THOUGH SHE WERE DRUNK. NOT THE MAUDLIN DRUNKENNESS SHE HAD BEEN PRONE TO WHEN WITH MITCH, BUT A EUPHORIA WHICH MADE HER FEEL WELL-NIGH INVULNERABLE, AS IF SHE HAD AT LAST LOCATED SOME BRIGHT AND INCORRUPTIBLE PART OF HERSELF, AND NO HARM WOULD EVER BEFALL HER AGAIN.

SHE HAD PREPARED HERSELF FOR FINDING ALL SAINTS IN RUINS, BUT SHE DID NOT. PERHAPS IT TOO COULD NOT BE TOPPLED, SHE MUSED; PERHAPS SHE AND IT WERE TWIN IMMORTALS. THE SUSPICION WAS REINFORCED BY THE GAGGLE OF FRESH WORSHIPPERS THE CHURCH HAD ATTRACTED.

THE ALTAR SERVERS, STANDING IN CLOSE PROXIMITY TO THE TENT, WORE MASKS AND GLOVES; THE HIGH PRIESTS--CHOSEN FEW WHO WERE ACTUALLY ALLOWED INTO THE HOLY OF HOLIES--WERE ENTIRELY GARBED IN PROTECTIVE SUITS.

S HE WATCHED FROM THE CORDON: THE SIGNS AND GENUFLECTIONS BETWEEN THE DEVOTEES, THE SLUICING DOWN OF THE SUITED MEN AS THEY EMERGED FROM BEHIND THE VEIL, THE FINE SPRAY OF FUMIGANTS WHICH FILLED THE AIR LIKE BITTER INCENSE.

WHY THE SUITS?

IN CASE IT'S CONTAGIOUS.

AFTER ALL THESE YEARS?

THEY DON'T KNOW WHAT THEY'VE GOT IN THERE.

DISEASES DON'T LAST, DO THEY?

IT'S A PLAGUE PIT. THEY'RE JUST BEING CAUTIOUS.

E LAINE'S TONGUE ITCHED TO SPEAK-- SHE COULD SAVE THEM THEIR INVESTIGATIONS WITH A FEW WORDS.

A FTER ALL, SHE WAS LIVING PROOF THAT WHATEVER PESTILENCE HAD DESTROYED THE FAMILIES IN THE CRYPT, IT WAS NO LONGER VIRULENT.

SHE HAD BREATHED THAT AIR, SHE HAD TOUCHED THAT MOLDY FLESH, AND SHE FELT HEALTHIER NOW THAN SHE HAD IN YEARS.

B UT THEY WOULD NOT THANK HER FOR HER REVELATIONS, WOULD THEY? THEY WERE TOO ENGROSSED IN THEIR RITUALS, PERHAPS EVEN EXCITED BY THE DISCOVERY OF SUCH HORRORS, THEIR TURMOIL FUELED AND FIRED BY THE POSSIBILITY THAT THIS DEATH WAS STILL LIVING. SHE WOULD NOT BE SO UNSPORTING AS TO SOUR THEIR ENTHUSIASM WITH A CONFESSION OF HER OWN RARE GOOD HEALTH.

WALTER!

WALTER!

WHY, ELAINE!

HAVE YOU HEARD WHAT THEY'VE FOUND?

OH YES.

NOW YOU'LL NEVER GET YOUR STONES.

I SUPPOSE NOT.

SHE WANTED TO TELL HIM THAT SHE'D SEEN THE PLAGUE PIT WITH HER OWN EYES, HOPING THE NEWS WOULD BRING A GLEAM TO HIS FACE, BUT THE CORNER OF THIS SUNLIT STREET WAS AN INAPPROPRIATE SPOT FOR SUCH TALK.

BESIDES, IT WAS ALMOST AS IF HE KNEW. HE LOOKED AT HER SO ODDLY, THE WARMTH OF THEIR PREVIOUS MEETING ENTIRELY GONE.

WHY DID YOU COME BACK?

JUST TO SEE.

I'M FLATTERED.

FLATTERED?

THAT MY ENTHUSIASM FOR MAUSOLEUMS IS INFECTIOUS.

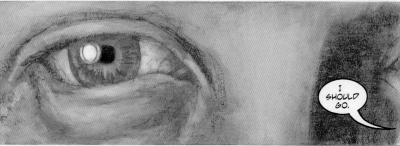

SUDDENLY ELAINE WAS CONSCIOUS OF HOW COLD HIS EYES WERE, AND HOW PERFECTLY SHINY. THEY MIGHT HAVE BEEN GLASS, SHE THOUGHT, AND HIS SKIN SUEDE, GLUED LIKE A HOOD OVER THE SUBTLE ARCHITECTURE OF HIS SKULL.

I SHOULD GO.

BUSINESS OR PLEASURE?

NEITHER. ONE OR TWO OF MY FRIENDS ARE ILL.

AH.

SHE HAD THE IMPRESSION THAT HE WANTED TO BE AWAY, THAT IT WAS ONLY FEAR OF FOOLISHNESS THAT KEPT HIM FROM RUNNING FROM HER.

PERHAPS I'LL SEE YOU AGAIN, SOMETIME.

I'M SURE.

AND TO YOUR FRIENDS--MY BEST REGARDS.

E VEN IF SHE HAD WANTED TO PASS KAVANAGH'S GOOD WISHES ALONG TO REUBEN AND SONJA, SHE COULD NOT HAVE DONE SO. HERMIONE DID NOT ANSWER THE TELEPHONE, NOR DID ANY OF THE OTHERS. THE CLOSEST SHE CAME WAS TO LEAVE A MESSAGE WITH REUBEN'S ANSWERING SERVICE.

T HE LIGHT-HEADEDNESS SHE'D FELT EARLIER IN THE DAY DEVELOPED INTO A STRANGE DREAMINESS AS THE AFTERNOON INCHED TOWARD EVENING. SHE ATE AGAIN, BUT THE FEAST DID NOTHING TO KEEP THE FUGUE STATE FROM DEEPENING.

S HE FELT QUITE WELL; THAT SENSE OF INVIOLABILITY THAT HAD COME UPON HER WAS STILL INTACT. BUT TIME AND AGAIN AS THE DAY WORE ON SHE FOUND HERSELF STANDING ON THE THRESHOLD OF A ROOM NOT KNOWING WHY SHE HAD COME THERE, OR WATCHING THE LIGHT DWINDLE IN THE STREET OUTSIDE WITHOUT BEING QUITE CERTAIN IF SHE WAS THE VIEWER OR THE THING VIEWED.

S HE WAS HAPPY WITH HER COMPANY THOUGH, AS THE FLIES WERE HAPPY. THEY KEPT BUZZING ATTENDANCE EVEN THOUGH THE DARK FELL.

dee DONG

S HE WENT TO THE DOOR OF HER FLAT, BUT COULDN'T MUSTER THE INQUISITIVENESS TO OPEN IT, STEP OUT INTO THE HALLWAY, AND ADMIT CALLERS.

IT WOULD BE HERMIONE AGAIN, MOST PROBABLY, AND SHE DIDN'T HAVE ANY APPETITE FOR GLOOMY TALK. DIDN'T WANT ANYBODY'S COMPANY, IN FACT, BUT THAT OF THE FLIES.

dee DONG dee DONG

T HE CALLERS INSISTED ON THE BELL; THE MORE THEY INSISTED THE MORE DETERMINED SHE BECAME NOT TO REPLY. IT WASN'T HERMIONE--THE VOICES SHE HEARD BELONGED TO NO ONE SHE RECOGNIZED.

JOEL PRUDHOE

ELAINE RIDER

ROBERT TOTERA

NOK NOK

'ELAINE? MISS RIDER?'

OF THE CONVERSATION THAT FOLLOWED SHE CAUGHT SUFFICIENT ONLY TO GRASP THE URGENCY OF THEIR MISSION, BUT HER DISHEVELED MIND HADN'T THE PERSISTENCE TO ATTEND TO THE DETAILS.

MISS RIDER!

NOK NOK

SHE WONDERED IF THEY COULD HEAR HER SMILING IN THE DARK-NESS. AT LAST--AFTER A FURTHER EXCHANGE WITH PRUDHOE-- THEY LEFT HER TO HERSELF.

SHE DIDN'T KNOW HOW LONG SHE SAT ON HER HAUNCHES BESIDE THE DOOR, BUT WHEN SHE STOOD UP AGAIN HER LOWER LIMBS WERE ENTIRELY NUMB, AND SHE WAS HUNGRY.

THE FLIES SEEMED TO HAVE PROCREATED IN THE INTERVENING HOURS; THEY CRAWLED ON THE TABLE AND PICKED AT HER SLOPS. SHE LET THEM EAT. THEY TOO HAD THEIR LIVES TO LIVE.

MISS *RIDER.* WAIT A MOMENT. I HAVE A MESSAGE FOR YOU.

THERE WERE *POLICEMEN* HERE. THEY WERE *LOOKING* FOR YOU.

OH. DID THEY SAY WHAT THEY WANTED?

TO TALK TO YOU. *URGENTLY.* TWO OF YOUR FRIENDS--

WHAT ABOUT THEM?

THEY *DIED.* THIS AFTERNOON. THEY HAVE SOME KIND OF *DISEASE.*

NO SOONER HAD ELAINE DECIDED TO TAKE SOME AIR, HOWEVER, THAN THE VIGILANT PRUDHOE WAS AT THE TOP OF THE STAIRS.

THEY LEFT THAT NUMBER FOR YOU TO CALL.

YOU'RE TO CONTACT THEM AS SOON AS POSSIBLE.

73f3941

FOR SOME REASON SHE WASN'T THINKING OF REUBEN OR SONJA--WHO, IT SEEMED, SHE WOULD NOT SEE AGAIN--BUT OF THE SAILOR, MAYBURY, WHO'D SEEN DEATH AND ESCAPED IT ONLY TO HAVE IT FOLLOW HIM LIKE A LOYAL DOG, WAITING ITS MOMENT TO LEAP AND LICK HIS FACE.

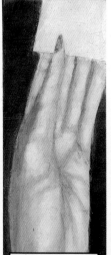

WAS THE TOUCH THAT HUNG SO INNOCENTLY AT THE END OF HER ARMS NOW LETHAL? WAS THAT WHAT THE DETECTIVES HAD COME TO TELL HER, THAT HER FRIENDS WERE DEAD BY *HER* GOOD OFFICES?

SUDDENLY SHE *KNEW,* KNEW IN HER MARROW, THAT HER PURSUERS WERE RIGHT IN THEIR SUSPICIONS, AND THAT ALL THESE DREAMY DAYS SHE HAD BEEN NURTURING A FATAL CHILD. HENCE HER HUNGER, HENCE THE GLOW OF FULFILLMENT SHE FELT.

SHE SAT IN THE SEMIDARKNESS, TRYING TO WORK OUT PRECISELY THE PLAGUE'S LOCATION.

WAS IT IN HER FINGERTIPS, IN HER BELLY, IN HER EYES? NONE, AND YET ALL OF THESE.

HER FIRST ASSUMPTION HAD BEEN WRONG. IT WASN'T A CHILD AT ALL: SHE DIDN'T CARRY IT IN SOME PARTICULAR CELL. IT WAS *EVERYWHERE*. SHE AND IT WERE SYNONYMOUS. THAT BEING SO, THERE COULD BE NO SLICING OUT OF THE OFFENDING PART, AS THEY HAD SLICED OUT HER TUMORS AND ALL THAT HAD BEEN DEVOURED BY THEM.

NOT THAT SHE WOULD ESCAPE THEIR ATTENTIONS FOR THAT FACT. THEY HAD COME LOOKING FOR HER, HADN'T THEY, TO TAKE HER BACK INTO THE CUSTODY OF STERILE ROOMS, TO DEPRIVE HER OF HER OPTIONS AND DIGNITY, TO MAKE HER FIT ONLY FOR THEIR LOVELESS INVESTIGATIONS?

THE THOUGHT REVOLTED HER; SHE WOULD RATHER DIE AS THE CHESTNUT-HAIRED WOMAN IN THE CRYPT HAD DIED, SPRAWLED IN AGONIES, THAN SUBMIT TO THEM AGAIN.

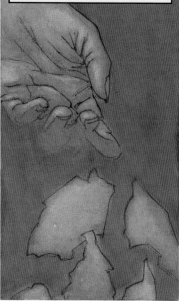

IT WAS TOO LATE FOR SOLUTIONS ANYWAY. THE MOVING MEN HAD OPENED THE DOOR AND FOUND DEATH WAITING ON THE OTHER SIDE, EAGER FOR DAYLIGHT. SHE WAS ITS AGENT, AND IT--IN ITS WISDOM--HAD GRANTED HER IMMUNITY, HAD GIVEN HER STRENGTH AND A DREAMY RAPTURE, HAD TAKEN HER FEAR AWAY. SHE, IN RETURN, HAD SPREAD ITS WORD, AND THERE WAS NO UNDOING THOSE LABORS: NOT NOW.

ALL THE DOZENS, MAYBE HUNDREDS, OF PEOPLE WHOM SHE'D CONTAMINATED IN THE LAST FEW DAYS WOULD HAVE GONE BACK TO THEIR FAMILIES AND FRIENDS, TO THEIR WORKPLACES AND THEIR PLACES OF RECREATION, AND SPREAD THE WORD YET FURTHER.

THEY WOULD HAVE PASSED ITS FATAL PROMISE TO THEIR CHILDREN AS THEY TUCKED THEM INTO BED...

...AND TO THEIR MATES IN THE ACT OF LOVE...

...PRIESTS HAD NO DOUBT GIVEN IT WITH COMMUNION...

...SHOPKEEPERS WITH CHANGE OF A FIVE-POUND NOTE.

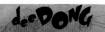

THEY HAD COME BACK FOR HER. AND, AS BEFORE, THEY WERE RINGING THE OTHER BELLS IN THE HOUSE. SHE COULD HEAR PRUDHOE COMING DOWNSTAIRS. THIS TIME HE WOULD KNOW SHE WAS IN. HE WOULD TELL THEM SO. THEY WOULD HAMMER AT THE DOOR, AND WHEN SHE REFUSED TO ANSWER--

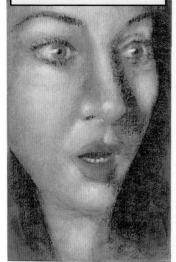

AS PRUDHOE OPENED THE FRONT DOOR SHE UNLOCKED THE BACK. AS SHE SLIPPED INTO THE YARD SHE HEARD VOICES AT THE FLAT DOOR, AND THEN THEIR RAPPING AND THEIR DEMANDS. SHE WAS ALREADY OUT OF HEARING RANGE BY THE TIME THEY HAD BEATEN DOWN THE DOOR.

SHE WANTED MOST OF ALL TO GO BACK TO ALL SAINTS, BUT SHE KNEW THAT SUCH A TACTIC WOULD ONLY INVITE ARREST. THEY WOULD EXPECT HER TO FOLLOW THAT ROUTE, COUNTING UPON HER ADHERENCE TO THE FIRST CAUSE. BUT SHE WANTED TO SEE DEATH'S FACE AGAIN, NOW MORE THAN EVER. TO SPEAK WITH IT. TO DEBATE ITS STRATEGIES. THEIR STRATEGIES. TO ASK WHY IT HAD CHOSEN HER.

WHAT WERE THEY DOING? PEEKING THROUGH HER UNDERWEAR AND HER LOVE LETTERS, MOST PROBABLY, EXAMINING THE SHEETS ON HER BED FOR STRAY HAIRS, AND THE MIRROR FOR TRACES OF HER REFLECTION.

BUT EVEN IF THEY TURNED THE FLAT UPSIDE DOWN, IF THEY EXAMINED EVERY PRINT AND PRONOUN, THEY WOULDN'T FIND THE CLUES THEY SOUGHT. LET THEM SEARCH.

THE LOVER HAD ESCAPED. ONLY HER TEARSTAINS REMAINED, AND FLIES AT THE LIGHT BULB TO SING HER PRAISES.

IT WAS ONLY NOW, IN THE RELATIVE HUSH, THAT SHE REALIZED SHE WAS NOT ALONE. FOOTSTEPS FOLLOWED HER, KEEPING A CAUTIOUS DISTANCE, BUT NEVER STRAYING FAR.

HAD THE TRACKERS FOLLOWED HER? WERE THEY HEMMING HER IN EVEN NOW, PREPARING TO SNATCH HER INTO THEIR CLOSED ORDER? IF SO, FLIGHT WOULD ONLY DELAY THE INEVITABLE. BETTER TO CONFRONT THEM NOW, AND DARE THEM TO COME WITHIN RANGE OF HER POLLUTION.

THMF

THMF

THMF

I FOLLOWED YOU.

ALL THE WAY FROM THE HOUSE?

HER INITIAL SHOCK WAS ALMOST IMMEDIATELY SUPERSEDED BY A SUDDEN COMPREHENSION OF WHY HE HAD PURSUED HER. HOW, HER WHIRLING THOUGHTS DEMANDED, HAD SHE NOT RECOGNIZED HIM SOONER, NOT REALIZED AT THAT FIRST MEETING, WHEN HE'D TALKED OF THE DEAD AND THEIR GLAMOUR, THAT HE SPOKE AS THEIR MAKER?

WHAT DID THEY TELL YOU? THE POLICEMEN. WHAT DID THEY SAY?

NOTHING I HADN'T ALREADY GUESSED.

YOU KNEW?

IN A MANNER OF SPEAKING, I MUST HAVE, IN MY HEART OF HEARTS. REMEMBER OUR FIRST CONVERSATION?

ALL YOU SAID ABOUT DEATH. SUCH EGOTISM.

YES. WHAT MUST YOU THINK OF ME.

IT MADE A KIND OF SENSE TO ME, EVEN THEN. I DIDN'T KNOW WHY AT THE TIME. DIDN'T KNOW WHAT THE FUTURE WOULD BRING--

WHAT DOES IT BRING?

DEATH'S BEEN WAITING FOR ME ALL THIS TIME, AM I RIGHT?

OH YES.

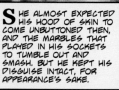

S HE ALMOST EXPECTED HIS HOOD OF SKIN TO COME UNBUTTONED THEN, AND THE MARBLES THAT PLAYED IN HIS SOCKETS TO TUMBLE OUT AND SMASH. BUT HE KEPT HIS DISGUISE INTACT, FOR APPEARANCE'S SAKE.

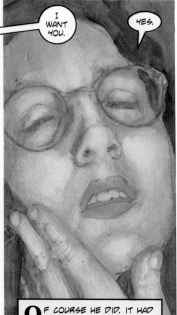

I WANT YOU.

YES.

O F COURSE HE DID. IT HAD BEEN IN HIS EVERY WORD FROM THE BEGINNING, BUT SHE HADN'T HAD THE WIT TO COMPREHEND IT. EVERY LOVE STORY WAS--AT THE LAST--A STORY OF DEATH; THIS WAS WHAT THE POETS INSISTED. WHY SHOULD IT BE ANY LESS TRUE THE OTHER WAY ABOUT?

T HEY COULD NOT GO BACK TO HIS HOUSE; THE OFFICERS WOULD BE THERE TOO, HE TOLD HER, FOR THEY MUST KNOW OF THE ROMANCE BETWEEN THEM. NOR, OF COURSE, COULD THEY RETURN TO HER FLAT.

S O THEY FOUND A SMALL HOTEL IN THE VICINITY AND TOOK A ROOM THERE.

WINTON HOTEL

VA ANCY

HER LOVER DIDN'T TAKE HIS EYES OFF HER FOR A SINGLE MOMENT, AS IF EVEN NOW HE EXPECTED HER TO TURN TAIL AND RUN AT THE MEREST FLAW IN HIS BEHAVIOR.

HIS TREATMENT OF HER LEFT LITTLE CAUSE FOR COMPLAINT. HIS KISSES WERE INSISTENT BUT NOT OVERPOWERING; HIS UNDRESSING OF HER-- EXCEPT FOR THE FUMBLING (A NICE HUMAN TOUCH, SHE THOUGHT)--WAS A MODEL OF FINESSE AND SWEET SOLEMNITY.

SHE WAS SURPRISED THAT HE HAD NOT KNOWN ABOUT HER SCAR, ONLY BECAUSE SHE HAD COME TO BELIEVE THIS INTIMACY HAD BEGUN ON THE OPERATING TABLE, WHEN TWICE SHE HAD GONE INTO HIS ARMS, AND TWICE BEEN DENIED THEM BY THE SURGEON'S BULLYING. BUT PERHAPS, BEING NO SENTIMENT- ALIST, HE HAD FORGOTTEN THAT FIRST MEETING.

IT'S BEAUTIFUL.

I ALMOST DIED UNDER THE ANESTHETIC.

THAT WOULD HAVE BEEN A WASTE.

WHAT DID THEY TELL YOU?

SHE HAD NOT BEEN TOUCHED IN MONTHS, EXCEPT BY DISINFECTED HANDS; HIS DELICACY WOKE SHIVERS IN HER. SHE WAS SO ENGROSSED IN PLEASURE THAT SHE FAILED TO REPLY TO HIS QUESTION.

WHAT DID THEY TELL YOU?

THEY LEFT A NUMBER FOR ME TO RING, SO THAT I COULD BE HELPED....

BUT YOU DIDN'T WANT HELP?

NO. WHY SHOULD I?

IT'S ALL RIGHT.

SHE HALF SAW HIS SMILE, THOUGH HER EYES WANTED TO FLICKER CLOSED ENTIRELY. HIS APPEARANCE FAILED TO STIR ANY PASSION IN HER; INDEED THERE WAS MUCH ABOUT HIS DISGUISE (THAT ABSURD BOW TIE, FOR ONE) WHICH SHE THOUGHT RIDICULOUS.

WITH HER EYES CLOSED, HOWEVER, SHE COULD FORGET SUCH PETTY DETAILS; SHE COULD STRIP THE HOOD OFF AND IMAGINE HIM PURE. WHEN SHE THOUGHT OF HIM THAT WAY, HER MIND PIROUETTED.

BE QUIET.

I THOUGHT I HEARD--

WHAT?

--I THOUGHT I HEARD THEM CALLING MY NAME.

WHO WOULD DO THAT? NOBODY KNOWS WE'RE HERE.

THEY CAME CLOSE, BUT THEY NEVER FOUND ME.

CLOSE?

COMING TO YOU.

SO VERY CLOSE. BUT I'M SWIFT, AND INVISIBLE.

AND ALWAYS NEAT.

SHE REMEMBERED THE CHAOS OF THE CRYPT, ITS INDIGNITIES, ITS DISORDERS.

AND THEN IT ALL STOPPED.

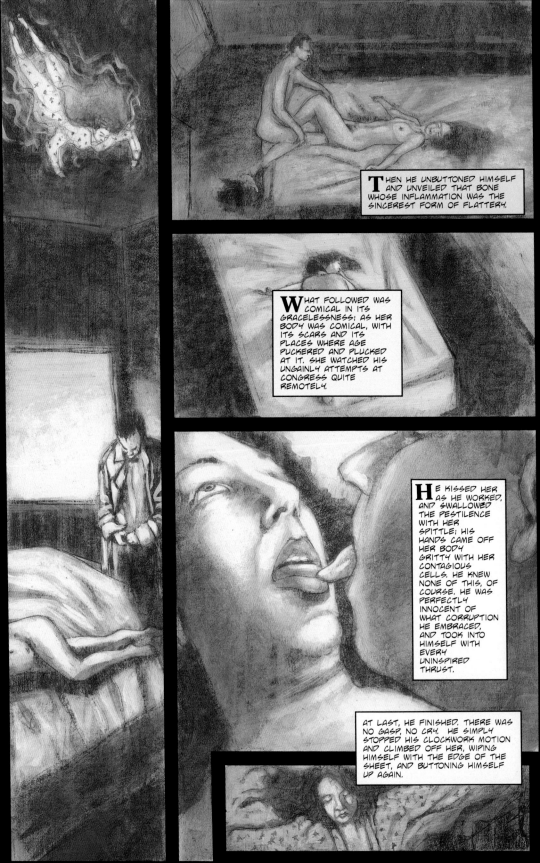

THEN HE UNBUTTONED HIMSELF AND UNVEILED THAT BONE WHOSE INFLAMMATION WAS THE SINCEREST FORM OF FLATTERY.

WHAT FOLLOWED WAS COMICAL IN ITS GRACELESSNESS; AS HER BODY WAS COMICAL, WITH ITS SCARS AND ITS PLACES WHERE AGE PUCKERED AND PLUCKED AT IT. SHE WATCHED HIS UNGAINLY ATTEMPTS AT CONGRESS QUITE REMOTELY.

HE KISSED HER AS HE WORKED, AND SWALLOWED THE PESTILENCE WITH HER SPITTLE; HIS HANDS CAME OFF HER BODY GRITTY WITH HER CONTAGIOUS CELLS. HE KNEW NONE OF THIS, OF COURSE. HE WAS PERFECTLY INNOCENT OF WHAT CORRUPTION HE EMBRACED, AND TOOK INTO HIMSELF WITH EVERY UNINSPIRED THRUST.

AT LAST, HE FINISHED. THERE WAS NO GASP, NO CRY. HE SIMPLY STOPPED HIS CLOCKWORK MOTION AND CLIMBED OFF HER, WIPING HIMSELF WITH THE EDGE OF THE SHEET, AND BUTTONING HIMSELF UP AGAIN.

S HE HAD
JOURNEYS TO
MAKE, REUNIONS
TO LOOK FORWARD
TO. BUT SHE DID
NOT WANT TO GO,
AT LEAST NOT
YET.

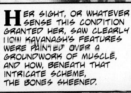

H ER SIGHT, OR WHATEVER
SENSE THIS CONDITION
GRANTED HER, SAW CLEARLY
HOW KAVANAGH'S FEATURES
WERE PAINTED OVER A
GROUNDWORK OF MUSCLE,
AND HOW, BENEATH THAT
INTRICATE SCHEME,
THE BONES SHEENED.

A H, THE BONE! HE WAS NOT
DEATH, OF COURSE, AND
YET HE WAS. HE HAD THE FACE,
HADN'T HE? AND ONE DAY,
GIVEN DECAY'S BLESSING, HE'D
SHOW IT. SUCH A PITY THAT A
SCRAPING OF FLESH CAME
BETWEEN IT AND THE NAKED
EYE.

COME
AWAY.

COME
AWAY.

A MOMENT,
ONLY A MOMENT
MORE.

VINTON HOTEL

VACANCY

WAS IT DAWN THAT WASHED THE SKY, OR THE ILLUMINATIONS? PERHAPS SHE HAD WATCHED HIM FROM THE CORNER OF THE ROOM LONGER THAN SHE'D THOUGHT--

--HOURS PASSING AS MOMENTS IN THE STATE SHE HAD SO RECENTLY ACHIEVED.

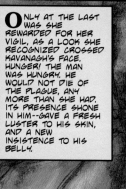

ONLY AT THE LAST WAS SHE REWARDED FOR HER VIGIL, AS A LOOK SHE RECOGNIZED CROSSED KAVANAGH'S FACE. HUNGER! THE MAN WAS HUNGRY. HE WOULD NOT DIE OF THE PLAGUE, ANY MORE THAN SHE HAD. ITS PRESENCE SHONE IN HIM--GAVE A FRESH LUSTER TO HIS SKIN, AND A NEW INSISTENCE TO HIS BELLY.

HA HA HA

HE HAD COME TO HER A MINOR MURDERER, AND WAS GOING FROM HER AS DEATH WRIT LARGE. SHE LAUGHED, SEEING THE SELF-FULFILLING PROPHECY SHE HAD UNWITTINGLY ENGINEERED.

FOR AN INSTANT HIS PACE SLOWED, AS IF HE MIGHT HAVE HEARD HER. BUT NO; IT WAS THE DRUMMER HE WAS LISTENING FOR, BEATING LOUDER THAN EVER IN HIS EAR AND DEMANDING, AS HE WENT, A NEW AND DEADLY VIGOR IN HIS EVERY STEP.

THE END

NEW MURDERS IN THE RUE MORGUE

WINTER, LEWIS DECIDED, WAS NO SEASON FOR OLD MEN. THE SNOW THAT LAY FIVE INCHES THICK ON THE STREETS OF PARIS FROZE HIM TO THE MARROW. WHAT HAD BEEN A JOY TO HIM AS A CHILD WAS NOW A CURSE. HE HATED IT WITH ALL HIS HEART; HATED THE SNOWBALLING CHILDREN (SQUEALS, HOWLS, TEARS); HATED, TOO, THE YOUNG LOVERS, EAGER TO BE CAUGHT IN A FLURRY TOGETHER (SQUEALS, KISSES, TEARS). IT WAS UNCOMFORTABLE AND TIRESOME, AND HE WISHED HE WAS IN FORT LAUDERDALE, WHERE THE SUN WOULD BE SHINING.

HE'D COME AT A SUMMONS FROM THE PAST, AND HE WOULD HAVE COME AS SWIFTLY, AND AS WILLINGLY, IF PARIS HAD BEEN BURNING.

BUT CATHERINE'S TELEGRAM, THOUGH NOT EXPLICIT, HAD BEEN URGENT, AND THE TIES OF FRIENDSHIP BETWEEN THEM HAD BEEN UNBROKEN FOR THE BEST PART OF FIFTY YEARS. HE WAS HERE FOR HER, AND FOR HER BROTHER PHILLIPE.

BESIDES, IT WAS HIS MOTHER'S CITY. SHE'D BEEN BORN ON THE BOULEVARD DIDEROT, BACK IN A TIME WHEN THE CITY WAS UNTRAMMELED BY FREE-THINKING ARCHITECTS AND SOCIAL ENGINEERS. NOW EVERY TIME LEWIS RETURNED TO PARIS HE STEELED HIMSELF FOR ANOTHER DESECRATION.

YEAR AFTER YEAR, MORE FINE HOUSES FOUND THEMSELVES RUBBLE. WHOLE STREETS SOMETIMES, GONE TO THE GROUND.

EVEN THE RUE MORGUE.

PERHAPS LEWIS WAS A LITTLE DISAPPOINTED NOT TO HAVE FOUND THE RUE MORGUE.

THERE WAS SOME DOUBT AS TO WHETHER THAT INFAMOUS STREET HAD EVER EXISTED IN THE FIRST PLACE, BUT LEWIS SAW LESS AND LESS PURPOSE IN DISTINGUISHING BETWEEN FACT AND FICTION.

FOR THE OLD, THE DISTINCTION WAS ACADEMIC.

AFTER ALL, IT WAS PART OF HIS HERITAGE.

MAYBE THE RUE MORGUE HAD EXISTED, AS DESCRIBED IN EDGAR ALLAN POE'S IMMORTAL STORY; MAYBE IT WAS PURE INVENTION. WHICHEVER, IT WAS NO LONGER TO BE FOUND ON A MAP OF PARIS.

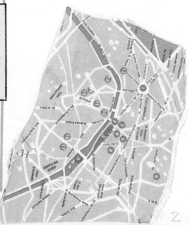

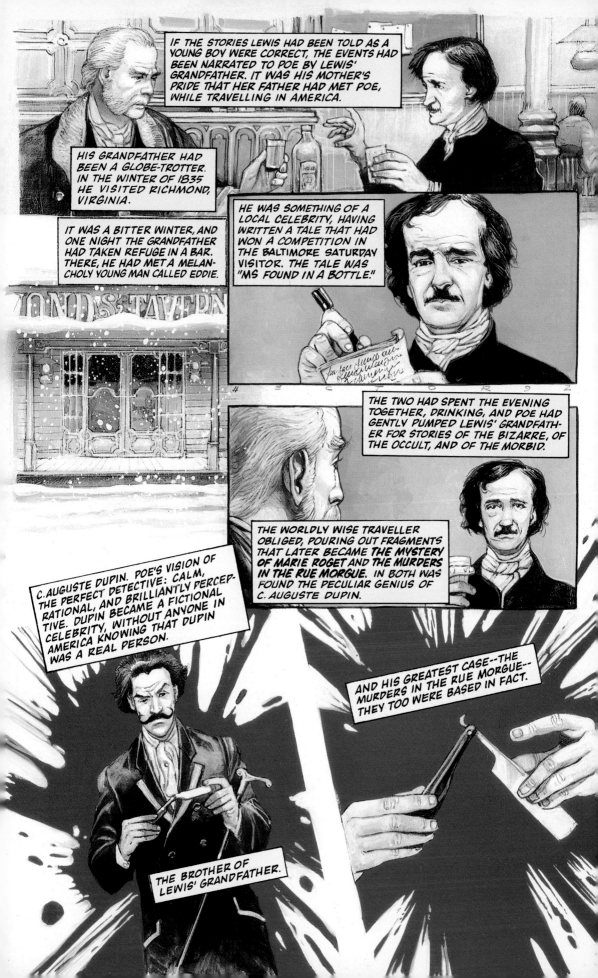

IF THE STORIES LEWIS HAD BEEN TOLD AS A YOUNG BOY WERE CORRECT, THE EVENTS HAD BEEN NARRATED TO POE BY LEWIS' GRANDFATHER. IT WAS HIS MOTHER'S PRIDE THAT HER FATHER HAD MET POE, WHILE TRAVELLING IN AMERICA.

HIS GRANDFATHER HAD BEEN A GLOBE-TROTTER. IN THE WINTER OF 1835 HE VISITED RICHMOND, VIRGINIA.

IT WAS A BITTER WINTER, AND ONE NIGHT THE GRANDFATHER HAD TAKEN REFUGE IN A BAR. THERE, HE HAD MET A MELANCHOLY YOUNG MAN CALLED EDDIE.

HE WAS SOMETHING OF A LOCAL CELEBRITY, HAVING WRITTEN A TALE THAT HAD WON A COMPETITION IN THE BALTIMORE SATURDAY VISITOR. THE TALE WAS "MS FOUND IN A BOTTLE."

THE TWO HAD SPENT THE EVENING TOGETHER, DRINKING, AND POE HAD GENTLY PUMPED LEWIS' GRANDFATHER FOR STORIES OF THE BIZARRE, OF THE OCCULT, AND OF THE MORBID.

THE WORLDLY WISE TRAVELLER OBLIGED, POURING OUT FRAGMENTS THAT LATER BECAME *THE MYSTERY OF MARIE ROGET* AND *THE MURDERS IN THE RUE MORGUE.* IN BOTH WAS FOUND THE PECULIAR GENIUS OF C. AUGUSTE DUPIN.

C. AUGUSTE DUPIN. POE'S VISION OF THE PERFECT DETECTIVE: CALM, RATIONAL, AND BRILLIANTLY PERCEPTIVE. DUPIN BECAME A FICTIONAL CELEBRITY, WITHOUT ANYONE IN AMERICA KNOWING THAT DUPIN WAS A REAL PERSON.

AND HIS GREATEST CASE--THE MURDERS IN THE RUE MORGUE-- THEY TOO WERE BASED IN FACT.

THE BROTHER OF LEWIS' GRANDFATHER.

TWO WOMEN HAD BEEN BRUTALLY KILLED IN THE RUE MORGUE.

THEY WERE MADAM L'ESPANAYE AND HER DAUGHTER MADEMOISELLE CAMILLE.

BOTH WOMEN OF GOOD REPUTATION, WHO LIVED QUIET LIVES.

THE DAUGHTER'S BODY HAD BEEN THRUST UP THE CHIMNEY; THE BODY OF THE MOTHER WAS DISCOVERED IN THE YARD.

NO APPARENT MOTIVE COULD BE FOUND, AND ALL THE OCCUPANTS CLAIMED TO HAVE HEARD THE MURDERER SPEAKING IN A DIFFERENT LANGUAGE.

THE FRENCHMAN WAS CERTAIN THE VOICE HAD SPOKEN SPANISH, THE ENGLISHMAN HAD HEARD GERMAN, THE DUTCHMAN THOUGHT IT WAS FRENCH. DUPIN NOTED THAT NONE OF THE WITNESSES ACTUALLY SPOKE THE LANGUAGE THEY CLAIMED TO HAVE HEARD.

ENGLISH
FRENCH
DUTCH
AMERICAN
HUMAN ←!
OTHER ←

DUPIN CONCLUDED THAT THE LANGUAGE WAS NO LANGUAGE AT ALL, BUT THE WORDLESS VOICE OF A WILD BEAST.

AN APE IN FACT, A MONSTROUS ORANG-OUTANG FROM THE EAST INDIAN ISLANDS. ITS TAWNY HAIRS HAD BEEN FOUND IN THE GRIP OF THE SLAIN MADAM L'ESPANAYE. ONLY ITS STRENGTH AND AGILITY MADE THE APPALLING FATE OF MADEMOISELLE CAMILLE PLAUSIBLE.

THE BEAST HAD BELONGED TO A MALTESE SAILOR, HAD ESCAPED, AND RUN RIOT IN THE BLOODY APARTMENT ON THE RUE MORGUE.

WHETHER TRUE OR NOT THE TALE HELD A GREAT ROMANTIC APPEAL FOR LEWIS. HE LIKED TO THINK OF HIS GREAT-UNCLE LOGICALLY PACING HIS WAY THROUGH THE MYSTERY UNDISTRESSED BY THE HYSTERIA AND HORROR AROUND HIM. HE THOUGHT OF THAT CALM AS ESSENTIALLY EUROPEAN, BELONGING TO A LOST AGE IN WHICH THE LIGHT OF REASON WAS STILL VALUED, AND THE WORST HORROR THAT COULD BE CONCEIVED OF WAS A BEAST WITH A CUT-THROAT RAZOR.

NOW, AS THE 20TH CENTURY GROUND THROUGH ITS LAST QUARTER, THERE WERE FAR GREATER ATROCITIES, ALL COMMITTED BY HUMAN BEINGS. THE HUMBLE ORANG-OUTANG HAD BEEN FOUND BY ANTHROPOLOGISTS TO BE A SOLITARY HERBIVORE.

THE TRUE MONSTERS WERE FAR LESS APPARENT, AND FAR MORE POWERFUL. THEIR WEAPONS MADE RAZORS LOOK PITIFUL, THEIR CRIMES WERE VAST. IN SOME WAYS LEWIS WAS GLAD TO BE OLD AND LEAVING THE CENTURY TO ITS OWN DEVICES.

YES, THE SNOW FROZE HIS MARROW. YES, TO SEE A YOUNG GIRL WITH THE FACE OF A GODDESS USELESSLY STIRRED HIS DESIRE. YES, HE FELT LIKE AN OBSERVER NOW INSTEAD OF A PARTICIPATOR.

BUT IT HAD NOT ALWAYS BEEN THAT WAY.

IN 1937, IN THE VERY ROOM WHERE HE NOW SAT, THERE HAD BEEN EXPERIENCE ENOUGH.

THEY HAD BEEN CARELESS THEN, IN BOTH SENSES OF THE WORD, LIVING ENDLESS LIVES IN PERFECT LEISURE.

IT WASN'T SO, OF COURSE. THE LIVES HAD NOT BEEN PERFECT, OR ENDLESS. BUT FOR A TIME--A SUMMER, A MONTH, A DAY--IT HAD SEEMED NOTHING IN THE WORLD WOULD CHANGE.

IN HALF A DECADE PARIS WOULD BURN, AND ITS PLAYFUL GUILT, WHICH WAS TRUE INNOCENCE, WOULD BE SOILED PERMANENTLY.

HIS THOUGHTS TURNED TO HIS RECENT NEW YORK EXHIBITION, IN WHICH HIS PAINTINGS HAD BEEN A BRILLIANT CRITICAL SUCCESS. AT THE AGE OF 73 FOX WAS A FETED MAN.

ADMIRERS AND BUYERS HAD SPRUNG UP LIKE MUSHROOMS OVERNIGHT, ALL TOO LATE, OF COURSE.

HE'D PUT DOWN HIS BRUSHES FOR THE LAST TIME FIVE YEARS AGO. NOW HE WAS MERELY A SPECTATOR.

WHEN THE TELEGRAM HAD COME FROM PARIS, BEGGING FOR HIS ASSISTANCE, HE HAD BEEN MORE THAN PLEASED TO SLIP AWAY FROM THE RING OF IMBECILES MOUTHING HIS PRAISE.

NOW HE WAITED IN THE DARKENING APARTMENT.

BUT CATHERINE DIDN'T COME.

NIGHT FELL. AT LAST, HE HEARD FOOTSTEPS IN THE HALL; EXCHANGED WHISPERS WITH THE HOUSEKEEPER.

IT WAS CATHERINE. AT LAST, IT WAS CATHERINE.

LEWIS, MY DARLING--

YOU LOOK WELL.

NO, I DON'T. IF I LOOK WELL IT'S AN INSULT TO PHILLIPE. HOW CAN I BE WELL WHEN HE'S IN SUCH TROUBLE?

SHE LOOKED OLDER THAN HE'D EXPECTED. HOW LONG WAS IT SINCE HE'D SEEN HER? FOUR YEARS OR FIVE? HER FRAGRANCE WAS THE SAME AS SHE ALWAYS WORE, AND IT REASSURED LEWIS WITH ITS PERMANENCE.

A TINY HESITATION. A FLICKER OF AN EYELID.

HE'S ACCUSED OF...MURDER.

IT'S TRUE, LEWIS. I COULDN'T TELL YOU BY TELEGRAM, YOU UNDERSTAND. I HAD TO SAY IT MYSELF.

MURDER. HE'S ACCUSED OF MURDER.

WHO?

A GIRL, OF COURSE. ONE OF HIS FANCY WOMEN.

HE STILL GETS AROUND, DOES HE?

SHE WAS NINETEEN. NATALIE PEREC. LONG RED HAIR. YOU REMEMBER HOW PHILLIPE LOVED REDHEADS?

THERE WAS A PAIN IN HIS TEMPLES, WHICH MIGHT GO IF HE CLOSED HIS EYES. BUT MAYBE SLEEP WAS JUST AN ESCAPE. HERE WAS SOMETHING EVEN HE COULDN'T BE A SPECTATOR TO.

WHERE IS HE?

THEY LOCKED HIM UP. THEY SAY HE'S DANGEROUS. THEY SAY HE COULD KILL AGAIN.

HE NEEDS TO SEE YOU. VERY BADLY.

THE OFFICER IN CHARGE OF THE INVESTIGATION WAS LESS THAN HELPFUL. LEWIS' CONTEMPT FOR THE SHODDILY DRESSED WEASEL MADE THE INTERVIEW CRACKLE WITH SUPPRESSED ANGER.

YOUR FRIEND IS A MURDERER, MONSIEUR FOX. IT IS AS SIMPLE AS THAT. THE EVIDENCE IS OVERWHELMING.

I CAN'T BELIEVE THAT.

BELIEVE WHAT YOU LIKE. HE WILL BE PUNISHED TO THE FULL EXTENT OF THE LAW.

WHAT EVIDENCE DO YOU HAVE AGAINST HIM?

NO OTHER PERSON WAS SEEN IN THE HOUSE AND ACCESS IS ONLY POS- SIBLE BY THE STAIRS--

AND THE BODY?

HORRIBLE. SKIN AND MUSCLE STRIPPED FROM THE BONE. ALL THE SPINE EXPOSED. BLOOD. MUCH BLOOD.

AN OLD MAN WOULD NOT BE CAPABLE--

IN OTHER RESPECTS HE SEEMS TO HAVE BEEN QUITE CAPABLE, OUI? THE LOVER, YES?

I UNDERSTAND YOUR CONFUSION, OUI? BUT YOU ARE WASTING YOUR TIME. A CRIME IS A CRIME. IT IS REAL, IT IS THE TRUTH.

TRUTH? YOU WOULDN'T KNOW THE TRUTH IF YOU TRIPPED OVER IT.

IT WAS PRECIOUS LITTLE SATISFACTION, BUT IT MADE LEWIS FEEL BETTER FOR AT LEAST FIVE MINUTES.

THE HOUSE ON THE RUE DES MARTYRS WAS NOT IN GOOD CONDITION. DOORS OPENED AS HE PASSED, BUT NOBODY TRIED TO STOP HIM.

THE ROOM WHERE THE ATROCITY HAD HAPPENED WAS LOCKED.

FRUSTRATED, HE MADE HIS WAY BACK DOWN THE STAIRS AND INTO THE BITTER AIR.

CATHERINE WAS BACK AT THE QUAI DE BOURBON.

WHAT'S WRONG?

I WENT TO PHILLIPE'S APARTMENT.

SO DID I. IT WAS LOCKED.

I HAVE THE KEY. PHILLIPE'S SPARE KEY. I JUST WANTED TO PICK UP A FEW CLOTHES FOR HIM.

"SOMEBODY ELSE WAS THERE."

"WHO?"

"I COULDN'T SEE. I DON'T KNOW EXACTLY... HE HAD A RAZOR, LEWIS. AN OPEN RAZOR, LIKE A BARBER."

SOMETHING JANGLED IN THE BACK OF LEWIS FOX'S MIND. AN OPEN RAZOR; A MAN DRESSED SO WELL HE COULDN'T BE RECOGNIZED.

DID HE HURT YOU?

I SCREAMED AND HE RAN AWAY...

MAYBE...A FRIEND OF THE GIRL... A BROTHER...

PERHAPS. BUT... THERE WAS SOMETHING ODD ABOUT HIM. HE SMELLED OF PERFUME, STANK OF IT, AND HE WALKED WITH SUCH MINCING LITTLE STEPS, EVEN THOUGH HE WAS HUGE.

TOMORROW I'LL SPEAK TO THE WEASEL.

INSPECTOR MARAIS. HAVE HIM SEARCH THE PLACE.

WEASEL?

DID YOU SEE PHILLIPE? IS HE WELL?

HE WANTS TO DIE, CATHERINE. HE'S GIVEN UP FIGHTING ALREADY, BEFORE HE GOES TO TRIAL.

BUT HE DIDN'T DO ANYTHING.

WE CAN'T PROVE THAT.

YOU'RE ALWAYS BOASTING ABOUT YOUR BLESSED DUPIN. *YOU* PROVE IT...

WHERE DO I START?

SPEAK TO SOME OF HIS FRIENDS, LEWIS. *PLEASE.* MAYBE THE WOMAN HAD ENEMIES.

JACQUES SOLAL STARED AT LEWIS THROUGH HIS ROUND-BELLIED SPECTACLES.

SHE HADN'T GOT ANY ENEMIES, NOT HER. OH, MAYBE A FEW WOMEN JEALOUS OF HER BEAUTY...

DO YOU THINK PHILLIPE MURDERED HER?

WHO KNOWS? AH, HE WAS MY FRIEND. IF I KNEW WHO HAD KILLED HER, I WOULD SAY SO.

SOLAL WAS AS UNINFORMATIVE AS HE WAS DRUNK, BUT, UNLIKELY AS IT SEEMED, CATHERINE HAD DESCRIBED THE RUNT ACROSS THE TABLE AS PHILLIPE'S CLOSEST FRIEND.

HE WAS A GENTLEMAN.

AND THE GIRL?

SHE WAS BEAUTIFUL, AND HE WAS IN LOVE WITH HER. SHE HAD OTHER ADMIRERS, OF COURSE. A WOMAN LIKE HER--

JEALOUS ADMIRERS?

WHO KNOWS?

AGAIN: WHO KNOWS? FOR THE FIRST TIME IN TEN YEARS PERHAPS A GOAL APPEARED IN LEWIS' LIFE-- AN AMBITION TO SHOOT THE INDIFFERENT "WHO KNOWS?" OUT OF THE AIR... TO DISCOVER WHAT HAD HAPPENED IN THAT ROOM ON THE RUE DES MARTYRS.

DO YOU REMEMBER IF THERE WERE ANY PARTICULAR MEN WHO FANCIED HER?

OH, YES. THERE WAS ONE. I NEVER KNEW HIS NAME. A BIG MAN. I SAW HIM OUTSIDE THE HOUSE THREE OR FOUR TIMES. THOUGH TO SMELL HIM YOU'D HAVE THOUGHT--

HE SMELLED? OF WHAT?

PERFUME, LEWIS. PERFUME.

SOMEWHERE IN PARIS THERE WAS A MAN WHO HAD KNOWN THE GIRL. JEALOUS RAGE HAD OVERCOME HIM. IT WAS AS CLEAR AS THAT.

PHILLIPE-- HE LIKED THE PICTURES.

HE CAME HERE, SOMETIMES, TO SEE THEM.

THE CUTTINGS WERE OLD, STAINED AND FADING. PURELY LOCAL INTEREST. ACCOUNTS OF A FIRE-BALL SEEN IN A NEARBY STREET. ANOTHER ABOUT A BOY OF TWO BURNED TO DEATH IN HIS COT.

SOME FAR OLDER THAN OTHERS, ATROCITIES, BIZARRE MURDERS, RITUAL RAPES.

AND ALMOST BURIED WAS A SEPIA PHOTOGRAPH SO ABSURD IT COULD HAVE COME FROM THE HAND OF MAX ERNST. A HALF RING OF GENTLEMEN WERE GROUPED AROUND THE VAST, BLEEDING BULK OF AN APE. THE FACES IN THE PICTURE BORE EXPRESSIONS OF MUTE PRIDE, OF ABSOLUTE AUTHORITY OVER THE DEAD BEAST.

WHAT IS THAT?

WHO KNOWS? WHO KNOWS?

IT WAS NOT THE APE OF POE'S STORY, THAT WAS CERTAIN. THAT TALE HAD BEEN TOLD IN 1835, AND THE PHOTOGRAPH WAS FAR MORE RECENT. BESIDES, THE APE IN THE PICTURE WAS A GORILLA: CLEARLY A GORILLA.

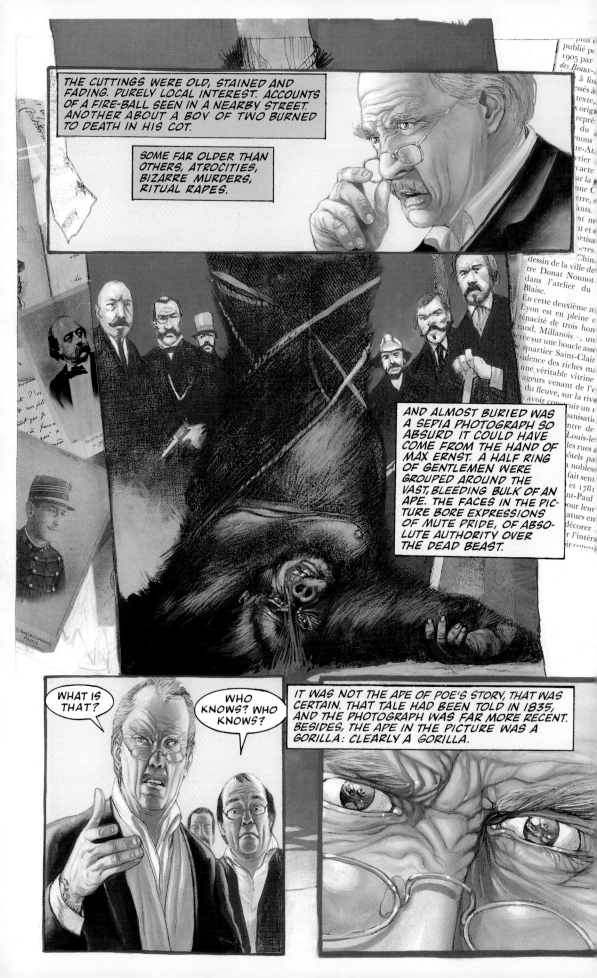

HAD HISTORY REPEATED ITSELF? HAD ANOTHER APE, A DIFFERENT SPECIES, BEEN LOOSED ON THE STREETS OF PARIS AT THE TURN OF THE CENTURY?

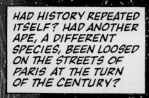

AND IF SO, IF THE STORY OF THE APE COULD REPEAT ITSELF ONCE...WHY NOT TWICE?

AS LEWIS WALKED THE IMAGINED EVENTS BECAME MORE ATTRACTIVE; WAS IT POSSIBLE THAT HE, THE NEPHEW OF DUPIN, MIGHT BECOME INVOLVED IN ANOTHER PURSUIT, NOT ENTIRELY DISSIMILAR FROM THE FIRST?

THE KEY TO PHILLIPE'S ROOM WAS ICY IN LEWIS' HAND.

IT WAS SATURDAY NIGHT, AND THERE WAS A LOT OF NOISE IN A NUMBER OF THE ROOMS.

THE KEY TURNED EASILY.

LEWIS REACHED FOR THE LIGHT SWITCH AND SNAPPED IT ON. NOTHING HAPPENED. THE BULB WAS SHATTERED.

HE HALF-THOUGHT ABOUT RETREATING.

SURELY IT WAS A MATTER OF A FEW MINUTES WORK TO FIND A CHANGE OF CLOTHES FOR PHILLIPE. OTHERWISE HE WOULD HAVE TO RETURN THE NEXT DAY. BETTER TO DO IT NOW AND SAVE HIS BONES.

THE NEXT DAY PARIS WOKE TO A BLIZZARD. FEW PEOPLE HAD EITHER THE NERVE OR MOTIVE TO STEP OUTSIDE INTO THE HOWLING GALE.

CATHERINE WANTED TO GO TO THE PRISON, BUT LEWIS INSISTED THAT HE GO ALONE. IT WAS NOT SIMPLY THE COLD WEATHER THAT MADE HIM CAUTIOUS ON HER BEHALF; HE HAD DIFFICULT WORDS TO SAY TO PHIL-LIPE, DELICATE QUES-TIONS TO ASK HIM. THE ONLY WAY TO SAVE PHILLIPE'S LIFE, IT SEEMED, WAS TO TRACE THE MAN. AND IF THAT MEANT DELVING INTO PHILLIPE'S SEXUAL AR-RANGEMENTS, THEN SO BE IT. BUT IT WASN'T A CONVERSATION HE, OR PHILLIPE, WOULD HAVE WANTED TO CONDUCT IN CATH-ERINE'S PRESENCE.

I WENT TO THE HOUSE TO FETCH THESE FOR YOU.

A BIG MAN, WITH A BEARD, WAS THERE ALREADY. DO YOU KNOW HIM? OR OF HIM?

NO.

PHILLIPE--

NO!

THE SAME MAN ATTACKED CATHERINE. WITH A RAZOR.

OR WAS GOING TO.

NO! HE WOULD NEVER HAVE TOUCHED HER. TELL HER NOT TO GO THERE AGAIN. NOT YOU EITHER.

YOU MUST TELL ME WHO THIS MAN IS, PHILLIPE.

YOU WOULDN'T UNDERSTAND, LEWIS. I COULDN'T EXPECT YOU TO UNDERSTAND.

JUST LET ME DIE... I WANT TO FORGET, WHY DO YOU TRY TO MAKE ME REMEM-BER? I WANT TO--

SHE WAS A WHORE.

WHORE!

LEWIS COULD MAKE NO SENSE OF THE TRANSFORMATION.

YOU BEGAN ALL THIS--

ME?

WITH YOUR STORIES. WITH YOUR DAMN DUPIN. IT WAS ALL A LIE--ALL STUPID LIES. WOMEN, MURDER--

YOU MEAN THE RUE MORGUE STORY?

YOU WERE SO PROUD OF THAT, WEREN'T YOU? ALL THOSE SILLY LIES. NONE OF IT WAS TRUE.

IT WAS A STORY, THAT'S ALL. DUPIN, THE RUE MORGUE, THE MURDERS... THE APE.

WHAT ABOUT THE APE?

THERE ARE BEASTS, LEWIS. SOME OF THEM ARE PITIFUL CIRCUS ANIMALS. THEY HAVE NO BRAINS... THEY ARE BORN VICTIMS. THEN THERE ARE OTHERS.

THE LOOK ON THE STRANGER'S FACE WAS OF UTTER DESPAIR, SO PITIFUL AS TO BE ALMOST TRAGIC.

OR RATHER, A PERFORMANCE OF TRAGEDY: AN ACTOR'S PAIN.

EVEN AS LEWIS STARED DOWN AT HIM, THE STRANGER RAISED HIS ARMS TO THE WINDOW IN A GESTURE THAT SEEMED TO BEG EITHER FORGIVENESS OR UNDERSTANDING, OR BOTH.

IT WAS TOO MUCH; ALL TOO MUCH.

IT WASN'T A MAN'S WALK, THAT ROLL, THAT SWAGGER.

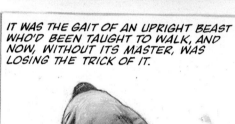

IT WAS THE GAIT OF AN UPRIGHT BEAST WHO'D BEEN TAUGHT TO WALK, AND NOW, WITHOUT ITS MASTER, WAS LOSING THE TRICK OF IT.

IT WAS AN APE.

OH GOD, OH-GOD, IT WAS AN APE.

19

I HAVE TO SEE PHILLIPE LABORTEAUX.

I'M SORRY, MONSIEUR.

HIS SISTER IS DYING. I BEG YOU TO HAVE SOME COMPASSION.

LEWIS HATED TALKING ABOUT CATHERINE IN SUCH A WAY, BUT IT WAS NECESSARY. IF HIS THEORY WAS CORRECT, HISTORY MIGHT REPEAT ITSELF BEFORE THE NIGHT WAS OUT.

YOU KEPT AN APE, DIDN'T YOU?!

ANSWER ME, PHILLIPE, I BEG YOU--BEFORE IT'S TOO LATE. DID YOU KEEP AN APE?

WHY?

IT WAS AN EXPERIMENT, THAT'S ALL IT WAS. AN EXPERIMENT.

YOUR DAMN STORIES. I WANTED TO SEE IF IT WAS TRUE THAT THEY WERE WILD. I WANTED TO MAKE A MAN OF IT...AND THAT WHORE. SHE SEDUCED IT.

YOU'LL KILL IT.

SO IT MURDERED HER?

IT WAS JEALOUS.

"IT BROKE INTO THE APARTMENT, WHILE CATHERINE WAS THERE. IT'S DANGEROUS NOW THAT IT HAS NO MASTER. DON'T YOU UNDERSTAND? THANK GOD, CATHERINE WAS UNHARMED."

"IT'S TRAINED--IT WOULDN'T HARM HER."

"AND THE GIRL?"

SEDUCED IT? WHERE IS THIS APE OF YOURS?

PERHAPS. I DON'T WANT TO THINK ABOUT IT.

YOU KNOW WHAT I MEAN, LEWIS. IT COULD BE A STORY. EXCEPT THAT MAYBE I MADE IT TRUE FOR A WHILE...DID YOU EVER THINK OF THAT? MAYBE I MADE IT TRUE.

ALL HE COULD THINK OF NOW WAS THAT PHILLIPE HAD IT EASY. HE'D TAKEN REFUGE IN PRE-TENDED GUILT, AND LOCKED HIMSELF AWAY WHERE MEM-ORY, AND REVENGE, AND THE TRUTH COULD NEVER TOUCH HIM AGAIN.

WHY HAVEN'T YOU TOLD THEM... HAD THE THING DESTROYED?

I DON'T KNOW IF IT'S TRUE. IT'S PROBABLY ALL A FICTION, JUST ANOTHER STORY.

IT WAS A TIRED DE-BATE: REALITY AND ILLUSION. EITHER A THING WAS, OR WAS NOT. LIFE WAS NOT A DREAM.

HERE--WHERE YOU CAN NEVER FIND HIM.

WHERE IS THE APE?

YOU DON'T KNOW WHAT YOU DID. YOU'LL NEVER KNOW.

HE HATED PHILLIPE AT THAT MOMENT FOR THE COWARD HE'D ALWAYS KNOWN HIM TO BE. NO LIFE COULD BE LIVED THE WAY HE'D LIVED IT WITHOUT A RECKONING COMING SOONER OR LATER. AND HERE IT WAS.

HE QUIETLY SPLASHED AND FOUNTAINED AWAY TO DEATH.

THAT NIGHT PHILLIPE WOKE. IN THE UTTER DARK HE CHEWED HIS WRIST UNTIL A PULSE OF BLOOD BUBBLED INTO HIS MOUTH.

21

THE SUICIDE WAS REPORTED IN A SMALL ARTICLE ON THE SECOND PAGE OF LE MONDE. THE BIG NEWS OF THE FOLLOWING DAY, HOWEVER, WAS THE SENSATIONAL MURDER OF A RED-HEADED PROSTITUTE IN A LITTLE HOUSE OFF THE RUE DE ROCHECHQUANT. MONIQUE ZEVACO HAD BEEN FOUND AT THREE O'CLOCK IN THE MORNING BY HER FLAT-MATE, HER BODY IN A STATE SO HORRIBLE AS TO "DEFY DESCRIPTION."

DESPITE THE ALLEGED IMPOSSIBILITY OF THE TASK, THE MEDIA SET ABOUT DESCRIBING THE INDESCRIBABLE WITH A MORBID WILL. EVERY LAST SCRATCH, TEAR AND GOUGING ON MONIQUE'S PARTIALLY NUDE BODY WAS CHRONICLED IN DETAIL. AS INDEED WAS THE APPEARANCE OF HER WELL-DRESSED, OVER-PERFUMED MURDERER, WHO HAD APPARENTLY WATCHED HER AT HER TOILET THROUGH A SMALL BACK WINDOW, THEN BROKEN IN AND ATTACKED MADEMOISELLE ZEVACO IN HER BATHROOM.

ONLY ONE COMMENTATOR MADE ANY CONNECTION BETWEEN THE MURDER AT THE RUE DES MARTYRS AND THE SLAUGHTER OF ZEVACO, AND HE FAILED TO PICK UP ON THE CURIOUS COINCIDENCE THAT THE ACCUSED PHILLIPE LABORTEAUX HAD THAT SAME NIGHT TAKEN HIS OWN LIFE.

LE MONDE

eau, telle ru
pots, ces fruits, c
constituent sa grammaire
lière, mais il est tout aussi clair
que l'essentiel est ailleurs, dans
la construction savamment dé-
centrée de la composition,
l'équilibre établi entre les plans
qui l'animent: échelonnement
des maisons, perspectives des
vasières, et toute la symphonie
subtile que jouent les objets, les
tables et les fonds de ses natures
mortes.
Ce sont là jeux subtils, si riches
de découvertes renouvelées que
l'artiste n'a jamais éprouvé le
besoin de changer radicalement
de manière pour échapper à
quelque grave crise, comme en
connaissent bien des créateurs:
non, ce qui lui impo e est bien
davantage de pour
qu'il sait être sie
delà cette

toriement la
, pour se situer
tières de l'abstrait.
Resterait à dire la su
monie des plus bel
qui comblent en no
de gravité et d
calme, comme les
les plus déchirante
Tel est le sens d
menée sans souci
des modes: la ré
Chenonceau pe
à novembre,
courbe dans tou
on saura gré à
Louis Menier,
Menier d'en av
nécessité.

ix feuilles r
Tony Garnier dé
e reçoit de gra
elle remporte
haine très co
de police.
le y règr
une v
e da
zon

qu   je me reç
re expliqué, mais de proposer un certain nombre
spondances qui s'établissent entre un incons
acharné à créer sa planète et mes propres réac
ns devant cette élaboration ambiguë."
ria, Venise, Lyon sont les lieux privilégiés du peintre
chromatique l

22

THE FUNERAL TOOK PLACE IN A STORM.

EVERY ONE IN PHILLIPE'S CIRCLE HAD DESERTED HIM, UNWILLING TO ATTEND THE FUNERAL OF A SUICIDE AND OF A SUSPECTED MURDERER. HIS WIT, HIS GOOD LOOKS, HIS INFINITE CAPACITY FOR CHARM, WENT FOR NOTHING IN THE END.

OVER THERE. UNDER THE TREE.

I'M GOING AFTER HIM.

HE WAS NOT, AS IT TURNED OUT, ENTIRELY UNMOURNED BY STRANGERS.

IT WAS AS THOUGH THE CREATURE WAS SOME MORBID ANGEL, COME TO HOVER A WHILE AND ENJOY THE GRIEF. IT WAS GROTESQUE, AND EERIE, THAT THIS THING SHOULD COME TO SEE PHILLIPE CONSIGNED TO THE FROZEN EARTH. WHAT DID IT FEEL? ANGUISH? GUILT?

IN A SHORT WHILE BOTH THE STRANGER AND HIS PURSUER WERE ERASED BY THE SNOW.

WHEN HE ARRIVED, SOLAL WAS NOT TO BE SEEN, BUT FRESH FOOTPRINTS IN THE POWDERY SNOW LED TO THE FRONT DOOR AND THEN, FOILED, WENT AROUND BACK OF THE HOUSE.

AS HE STEPPED INTO THE YARD BEHIND THE HOUSE HE REALIZED HE HAD COME WITHOUT A WEAPON.

THEN IT WAS GONE.

THE DOOR WAS NOT LOCKED. AS LEWIS STEPPED INSIDE THE STENCH STRUCK HIM... THE SICKLY SWEET SMELL OF ROTTEN FRUIT MINGLED WITH THE CLOYING COLOGNE: ZOO AND BOUDOIR.

LEWIS THOUGHT OF THE RAZOR. WAS THAT WHY IT HAD BEEN IN PHIL-LIPE'S ROOM?

ITS DAYS OF INNO-CENCE HAD GONE: IT COULD NEVER BE AN UNAMBITIOUS BEAST AGAIN. TRAPPED IN ITS NEW PERSONA, IT HAD NO CHOICE BUT TO CONTINUE IN THE LIFE ITS MASTER HAD AWOKEN ITS TASTE FOR.

LEWIS HAD THE IMPRES-SION THAT IT WAS PREPARING ITSELF FOR THE OUTSIDE WORLD, AND THE SIGHT WAS TOUCHING AS MUCH AS INTIMIDATING.

BUT THE BEAST WAS ABOUT OTHER BUSINESS.

JACQUES SOLAL WAS NOT THERE.

SOLAL?

UNABLE TO LEAVE JACQUES YET UNABLE TO MOVE HIM FAR, HE DID NOTHING AT ALL.

WAITING, IN A DREAMY HALF-LIFE, FOR THE END OF THE WORLD.

THEN, IT CAME HOME NOISILY LIKE A DRUNKEN MAN.

THERE WAS A VOICE IN THE ROOM, A WOMAN'S VOICE. THROUGH THE CRACK LEWIS COULD SEE THE BEAST, AND A RED-HAIRED YOUNG WOMAN WITH HIM.

YOU'VE GOT MORE! OH YOU SWEETIE!

WHERE DID YOU GET ALL THIS? OKAY, IF YOU DON'T WANT TO TELL ME, IT'S FINE BY ME.

IT'S SO...HOT...IN HERE.

SHALL I TAKE EVERYTHING OFF? YOU DON'T SAY MUCH, DO YOU?

LEWIS BEGAN TO FEEL DIZZY AGAIN. HIS LOWER LIMBS WERE NOW COMPLETELY NUMB. YET HE DIDN'T DARE MOVE.

WHAT EXPRESSION DID THAT SHAVED FACE WEAR? WAS THERE LUST IN ITS EYES, OR DOUBT?

WAS THIS PHILLIPE'S DOING TOO, OR HAD THE APE STOLEN THE STUFF FOR HIS OWN PURPOSES? DID HE REGULARLY SEDUCE REDHEADED PROSTITUTES WITH DRUGS?

THE APE WAS CAPABLE OF ANYTHING, LEWIS KNEW THAT. IF HE WAS DISCOVERED, WHAT MIGHT IT CHOOSE TO DO TO HIM AND THE GIRL?

THE AGONY WAS BECOMING UNBEARABLE. HE BEGAN TO THINK HE WOULD DIE IN THIS PATHETIC HIDING PLACE, WHILE THE APE MADE LOVE.

IT WAS TOO MUCH. WAS THIS DEATH? THE LIGHTS IN THE HEAD, THE WHINE IN HIS EARS? IT SEEMED TO GO ON FOREVER, INVADING HIS HEAD. SIGHS, LAUGHTER, LITTLE SHRIEKS.

AT LAST, DARKNESS.

PHILLIPE? PHILLIPE, WHO'S THIS?

AH...PHILLIPE... PLEASE. DO YOU WANT ME TO GO WITH THIS ONE AS WELL?

I WILL IF YOU WANT. JUST GIVE ME BACK THE PILLS.

LEWIS.

THE OLD MAN SHOULD BE READY FOR ANYTHING. EVEN TO BE GREETED AS A FRIEND OF A FRIEND BY THE BEAST THAT LOOMED IN FRONT OF HIM.

IT HAD COME TO THIS--OFFERED A HUMAN WOMAN BY THIS NAKED APE. IT WAS THE LAST, GOD HELP HIM, THE VERY LAST CHAPTER IN THE FICTION HIS GREAT-UNCLE HAD BEGUN. FROM LOVE TO MURDER BACK TO LOVE AGAIN.

LEWIS.

THE LOVE OF AN APE FOR A MAN. HE HAD CAUSED IT, WITH HIS DREAMS OF FICTIONAL HEROES, STEEPED IN ABSOLUTE REASON. HE HAD COAXED PHILLIPE INTO MAKING REAL THE STORIES OF A LOST YOUTH.

HE WAS TO BLAME.

AREN'T YOU STAYING?

THIS THING...

LEWIS.

HE'S NOT CALLED PHILLIPE. HE'S NOT EVEN HUMAN.

NOT THIS POOR STRUTTING APE, LOST BETWEEN THE JUNGLE AND THE STOCK EXCHANGE; NOT PHILLIPE, WANTING TO BE YOUNG FOREVER; CERTAINLY NOT COLD CATHERINE, WHO AFTER TONIGHT WOULD BE COMPLETELY ALONE. IT WAS HIM. LEWIS.

PLEASE YOURSELF.

THIS TIME, INSTEAD OF COMING OUT AS A SORT OF GRUNT-WORD, IT WAS PHILLIPE'S VOICE, PERFECTLY.

NOT PLEADING, NOT DEMANDING. SIMPLY NAMING, FOR THE PLEASURE OF NAMING, AN EQUAL.

IT WAS A CLEAR-HEAVEN DAY; THE LAST OF THE WINTER'S SNOW HAD FALLEN, AND THE THAW WOULD BEGIN BY NOON.

BIRDS, EXHULTING IN THE SUDDEN SUN, SWOOPED OVER THE SACRÉ COEUR. PARIS BEGAN TO UNDRESS FOR SPRING, ITS VIRGIN WHITE TOO SPOILED TO BE WORN FOR LONG.

WHO WAS THAT?

WHO KNOWS.

IN MID-MORNING, A YOUNG WOMAN WITH RED HAIR, HER ARM LINKED IN THAT OF A LARGE UGLY MAN, TOOK A LEISURELY STROLL TO THE STEPS OF THE SACRÉ COEUR.

THE SUN BLESSED THEM. BELLS RANG.

IT WAS A NEW DAY.

FIN

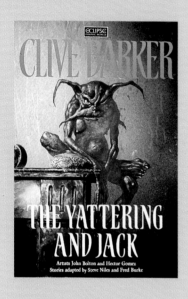

CLIVE BARKER'S

THE YATTERING AND JACK

Adapted by Steve Niles
Illustrated by John Bolton

A DARKLY HILARIOUS and weirdly perceptive tale of the devil at work from the acclaimed fantasist and master of horror fiction, Clive Barker.

Beelzebub sends his underling the Yattering to claim the soul of Jack Polo, pickle salesman. But in the Polo residence where the Yattering is bound, nothing doing. Polo's response, even to disaster, is merely to sigh, '*Que sera sera*'. The Yattering is going crazy. He must goad Polo to lunacy, the Old One insists. Polo was promised by his mother to the Lord of the Flies. And what match is a chronically dull pickle salesman for hell's own spawn . . . ? Find out.

Included in the same volume, a graphic adaptation of Clive Barker's short story *How Spoilers Bleed,* adapted by Steve Niles and Fred Burke, and illustrated by Hector Gomez. It tells of the gory revenge visited on white destroyers of the Brazilian jungle by the dying indigenous people of the Amazon basin. It is a punishment that fits the crime, incredibly unpleasant . . .

Clive Barker's bestselling works of fiction include *The Books of Blood, The Damnation Game, Weaveworld, Cabal, The Great and Secret Show,The Hellbound Heart , Imajica* and *The Thief of Always.* Not only is he prodigiously talented as a writer, he also produces and directs memorable films such as the *Hellraiser* trilogy, *Nightbreed* and *Candyman,* and is himself a spectacular visual artist. The illustrators he chooses to work with, therefore, John Bolton and Hector Gomez, are equally brilliant.

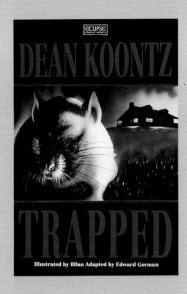

DEAN KOONTZ

TRAPPED

Adapted by Edward Gorman
Illustrated by Anthony Bilau

THE FIRST EVER graphic adaptation of a story
by the master of chilling fiction and chronicler of
midnight's menace, Dean Koontz.

Laboratory rats locked in a cage together - originally
they were kept in individual cages, but their aggressive
behaviour was so disturbing that they were put together
in the hope of quieting them. Instead it gives them the
chance they've been waiting for. They break out on a
stormy winter night. These are smart rats,
bioengineered and hostile, for some reason, to
humans. Perhaps because they were trapped . . .

But no longer. They take over the nearby house of
Meg Lassiter, two years a widow and mother to
Tommy, aged ten and with his leg in plaster from a
skiing fall. Meg and Tommy are trapped, now . . .
the rats' first victims.

Dean Koontz's inimitable style permeates the graphic
form, spreading evil and terror - and confronting them
with the force of a mother's need to protect her child.

Adapted by Edward Gorman and illustrated by
Anthony Bilau, this story of fear unleashed is realistic,
unnerving and moving.

NEIL GAIMAN

MIRACLEMAN: THE GOLDEN AGE

Illustrated by Mark Buckingham

NEIL GAIMAN'S spectacular, mysterious, luminously strange and compelling saga of the all-British superhero and deity, Miracleman. *The Golden Age* is the age of miracles unimagined. It is the age of gods among men. It is the age of truth in which everything is what it seems, and nothing is as it was imagined.

'A work that transforms the superhero genre into something strange, wonderful, and politic. Excellent stuff!'

ALAN MOORE

MIRACLEMAN was given new life by Alan Moore, known as the King of the graphic novel, in the early 1980s. His and Gaiman's work is assessed in the critique below by Samuel R. Delany, author of *Dhalgren*, the *Nevèrÿon* series, and other science fiction masterpieces.

'Moore and Gaiman are the two writers who have done more to change the idea of what comics are and can be than anyone since . . . well, certainly since I started reading them in the 1940s. Reading Moore, followed by Gaiman, I found myself for the first time deeply, consistently, intensely interested in these comic book writers *as writers*. With that interest came a revision in the idea of what comics could be; they could be *written*, not just in a craftsman-like manner adequate to the visuals. The writing could be brilliant in itself. Here were writers with the range of language from silence to song - the whole of language with which to put across their stories. And the stories themselves! Gaiman's six entwined tales in *The Golden Age* come like sapphires afloat on a super-cooled liquid. They unfold like haiku. The voices they speak with are real. Their lambent characters, yearning both for bits of yesterday and portents of tomorrow, will linger with you long.'

SAMUEL R. DELANY

CLIVE BARKER'S
REVELATIONS

Adapted by Steve Niles
Illustrated by Lionel Talaro

ANOTHER CLIVE BARKER story of living mayhem
and dying faith adapted for the graphic form by
Steve Niles and illustrated by Lionel Talaro.

A murder thirty years ago, to the night, haunts the
motel room where it happened - and where evangelist
John Gyer and his unhappy wife Virginia are staying.
Virginia senses the ghosts of Buck and Sadie Durning
are near. But her dependence on pills to alleviate the
oppressive effect her husband's "goodness" has on her
lead her only to hideous dreams of violence. Observing
her, the ghost Sadie, who was executed for the murder
of her husband, is moved to sympathy. She is unre-
pentant, even though tonight she and the ghost of her
husband have returned to the Cottonwood Motel to
attempt a reconciliation beyond the grave. Virginia's
problem is more compelling to her than Buck's lustful
ghost. Before the clouds part to reveal a full moon,
the blood-letting, the inevitable tragedy, will come to
pass, again.

Clive Barker, the supreme fantasist, mixes life and death
in a heady cocktail. Included in the same volume, an
adaptation of his sinister story, *Babel's Children*,
illustrated by Hector Gomez and adapted by
Steve Niles.

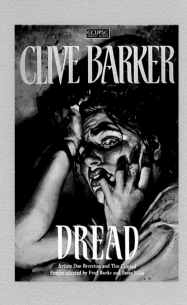

CLIVE BARKER'S
DREAD

Adapted by Fred Burke
Illustrated by Dan Brereton

WHAT DO YOU REALLY DREAD? Quaid, a student of philosophy, is interested to know. *Very* interested - as a hungry wolf is interested in red meat. Forget philosophy. Dread is at the heart of life. For Quaid, there is no delight the equal of dread, as long as it's someone else's. Cheryl Fromm's, for instance. Cheryl is bright, beautiful, dread-free, so she thinks. Even so, Quaid will teach her the meaning of fear . . . deliver her into dread. Quaid's friend Stephen Grace is sworn to silence on the Cheryl affair, but that won't save him, or Cheryl; and Quaid, of course, is both damned and doomed . . . to live the long night of his own dread. It is right to fear the darkness behind the door. No one escapes it. Open the door . . . to dread.

Adapted by Fred Burke and superbly, hauntingly illustrated by Dan Brereton, this is a graphic novel to linger over in appalled admiration at the extent of Clive Barker's understanding of his subject.

Also included in this volume, a graphic adaptation of Clive Barker's story, *Down Satan*. Adapted by Steve Niles and boldly illustrated by Tim Conrad, it tells of an atrocity waiting to happen: the New Hell built by one of the world's richest men to tempt the devil himself.